The Drugs Myth

The Drugs Myth

Why the drug wars must stop

Vernon Coleman

GREEN
PRINT

First published in 1992 by
Green Print
an imprint of The Merlin Press
10 Malden Road, London NW5 3HR

ISBN 1 85425 075 2

Phototypeset by Computerset Ltd., Harmondsworth, Middlesex

Printed in England by Biddles Ltd., Guildford, Surrey on recycled
paper

Contents

Dedication

To Barrie and Pat

1 | We are all addicts

The problem in perspective. We are all addicts. Whenever a drug user is taken to court the chances are high that the people involved in the prosecution – the judges and the police officers – will be using and addicted to more dangerous substances than the defendant in the dock.

Have you ever drunk a cup of coffee to help yourself wake up in the morning? Have you ever made yourself a cup of tea when you have been feeling physically or mentally tired? Have you ever been so bored, lonely or fed up that you have eaten a bar of chocolate or a biscuit when you knew that you were not hungry? Have you ever taken a sleeping tablet to help you get a good night's rest? Have you ever taken a pill to help calm your nerves prior to an aeroplane flight, a trip to the dentist or an important social event? Have you ever smoked a cigarette or a cigar? Have you ever drunk a glass of sherry, champagne, beer or wine?

If you have answered 'yes' to any of those questions – and of course you have! – then you know what it is like to need to use a chemical to help you put up with or overcome your daily problems or to alter your mood. If you use any of the substances I have mentioned above on a regular basis, then you are probably an addict. Alcohol, tobacco and caffeine are much more addictive and hazardous to your health than some illegal substances. The surprising but inescapable truth is that most people are addicted to something.

The Drugs Myth

Drug use is accepted as normal in modern society. Governments subsidize the production of tobacco and take a substantial profit on the sale of tobacco and alcohol. Many religious ceremonies involve the use of alcohol. Respectable housewives organize coffee mornings and share pots of tea together. It is, therefore, hardly surprising that drug abuse is not just commonplace but is the biggest epidemic of the twentieth century and by far the most important cause of illness and death in the western world.

Everyone does it: I doubt if there is a policeman, judge or politician anywhere in the world who has not used drugs at least once in his or her life. Most of those who oppose the use of drugs such as cocaine, heroin and cannabis are probably hooked on drugs which are far more dangerous than most illegal substances.

The fact that the use of some drugs is regarded as legal while the use of others is deemed illegal complicates the subject of drug abuse enormously. There is no logic in the laws which decide which substances are legal and which are illegal. Many of the world's most dangerous substances are perfectly legal while some relatively innocuous substances are illegal. Substances such as alcohol which are legal in one country will be illegal in another. Drugs are put into 'legal' or 'illegal' categories through an illogical, bizarre, irrational and entirely arbitrary selection system which depends more upon personal preferences, prejudices and commercial expediency than upon rational thought. The result is that in any court where an individual is being tried for possessing or using an illegal drug, the chances are high that the majority of those responsible for ensuring that the law is applied will be addicted to substances which are far more dangerous than the substance which has been used by the defendant.

Putting drugs into 'legal' and 'illegal' categories has not made much difference to the number of people prepared to try them. Laws which are patently abused or based on weak foundations get very little respect and the laws which are designed to limit drug use get about as much respect as the laws which govern the speed of motor cars on motorways. A recent survey in America showed that 59 per cent of American doctors have used illegal mood-altering drugs while 77 per cent of medical students have used them. Around a third of medically qualified Americans use mood altering drugs regularly. Doctors are cutting down their consumption of tobacco – which they recognize as being extremely dangerous – but they are not cutting down their use of illegal drugs which they consider to be less harmful.

And other citizens seem to agree with them. Experts estimate that an astonishing twenty million Americans use marijuana regularly while seventeen million have experimented with cocaine and half a million regularly use heroin. A few years ago a survey by the *Ladies' Home Journal* showed that a third of American women under the age of twenty-five years old had taken cocaine. In 1962 American statistics showed that only four per cent of people between the ages of eighteen and twenty five had smoked marijuana. Twenty years later, after a programme of suppression that had cost billions of dollars, sixty-four per cent of people in the same age group had tried it. Drug prices have consistently fallen, despite attempts to reduce the quantities available, and the purity of illegal drugs goes up as the price comes down.

In 1978 a White House presidential adviser on drugs reported that one in nine high school seniors were using so much marijuana every day that they were 'stoned' or under its influence from the time they got up in the morning until they went to bed at night. In the United Kingdom the figures are more vague. The official figures suggest that around 50,000 people are addicted to heroin and cocaine but officials suggest that the real figure is probably ten times as high. It is impossible to obtain accurate figures because people who use illegal drugs do not usually talk openly about their 'crimes'. That is another problem: drugs that are illegal cannot be regulated and the extent of their use cannot possibly be estimated accurately. All around the world illegally obtained drugs are being used by a constantly growing number of people – most of whom would probably describe themselves as normal and law-abiding.

Drug smuggling is now the biggest and most profitable industry in the world. According to *The Economist* cocaine is the most profitable article of trade in the world. In California the cash value of the cannabis crop is said to be greater than the value of the grape crop – supposedly the state's leading agricultural product. The world's drug business is estimated (by a United States senate sub-committee) to be worth over $500 billion a year – with $475 billion tax-free profits. Just 'laundering' that amount of money is very big business and many of the world's most apparently respectable banks are involved. There are drug dealers whose annual earnings exceed those of many countries. When Johnny Carson told an Oscar presentation audience that 'The biggest moneymaker in Hollywood last year was Colombia. Not the studio – the country', he probably was not far from the truth. Drugs are so light and so easily transportable that they are now preferred to diamonds as an international currency. In 1978 when thousands of Iranians fled their country during the Ayatollah Khomeini's revolution, many took their wealth with them as heroin because it was lighter than the equivalent in currency.

Millions of people are being turned into criminals by a series of inexplicable laws which are also threatening our civil liberties and encouraging violence on a hitherto unimagined scale. Despite strenuous and expensive efforts to uphold these laws the world's law enforcement agencies have failed, are failing and will clearly continue to fail. They are failing partly because the demand for drugs has always been there. Laws outlawing drug use are as doomed as laws outlawing prostitution. They are also failing partly because the laws which exist are widely disliked. (Laws which outlaw drug use are as unpopular and as widely disregarded as the laws which exist supposedly to control the speed of motor cars on the roads). And they are failing because they are overtly hypocritical and uniquely ill thought out. People *know* that tobacco is more dangerous than marijuana and so they have no respect at all for a law which flouts commonsense.

Laws which prohibit the purchase, possession or use of drugs do not, it seems, have very much influence on the use of those drugs but they do turn the people who use them into criminals, thereby creating a whole range of new problems. The credibility of the law is damaged and the number of people with no respect for the law is increased. Irrational laws which allow the free sale of some dangerous drugs and ban others (far less dangerous) drugs push millions of otherwise law-abiding

4

citizens into close contact with criminals, make them vulnerable to blackmail and expose them to other forms of crime. Thousands of serious crimes are committed by individuals who want (or need) the money to pay for extremely expensive illegal drugs. It is estimated that Britain's addicts steal at least £20 million worth of goods a day to pay for the drugs they buy. The vast untaxed profits made by those who produce, import and market illegal drugs have encouraged new levels of violence in the underworld and have helped create and sustain a remarkable series of super-rich criminal fraternities.

Do not assume by what you have read that I am in favour of drug use or in sympathy with drug abuse. I recognize that drug addiction is now a major world-wide problem. Several years ago in my book *Addicts and Addictions* I described drug addiction as 'the twentieth-century plague' and I think the description is still valid. There are addicts in every country in the world. For countless decades addictions have wrecked homes, destroyed careers and ruined lives in a hundred different ways. Back in 1970 more Americans were evacuated from Vietnam for drug-related reasons than for war injuries. In 1978 Lester Wolff, then chairman of the United States House of Representatives Select Narcotics Abuse and Control Committee, estimated that ten to twenty per cent of the two hundred thousand troops America had in Europe were taking 'hard' narcotics regularly. This was, he admitted, equivalent to having almost two divisions using drugs. By the mid 1980s a Department of Defense survey showed that 31.4 per cent of American servicemen in Europe were using drugs such as cannabis, cocaine and LSD and one in ten admitted to working under the influence of drugs. There have been many cases of drug abuse aboard nuclear submarines and at nuclear bases.

The cost of drug abuse is usually regarded as consisting of treating addicts and policing airports and coastal areas. But it is a much bigger problem than that. The *total* cost of drug use and abuse is almost impossible to quantify. During the 1980s Roger Smith, chairman of General Motors, reported that absenteeism, largely due to drug and alcohol abuse, cost his company one billion dollars a year. The American Department of Health and Human Services has estimated that drug use in factories and offices costs America at least twenty-five billion dollars a year.

The Drugs Myth

Despite all the money and effort put into controlling drug abuse
– most of it into more and more pieces of legislation and
increasingly sophisticated police forces – the problem is getting
worse.

According to Dr William Pollin, Director of the National
Institute on Drug Abuse in the United States, more than one
quarter of all deaths in America are premature and caused by
addiction. But it is *legal* drugs which cause the vast majority of
the deaths. In Britain tobacco kills 100,000 people a year while
there are 700,000 alcohol addicts and 700,000 families struggling
to cope with the problems alcohol addiction produces. There
must surely be something fundamentally wrong with our present system. In America approximately 100,000,000 people drink
alcohol and about 60,000,000 smoke tobacco – both legal substances. The combined death rate for these two drugs is around
500,000 people a year. In the developed world the average adult
spends around $325 a year on tobacco and $750 a year on
alcohol; cigarette smokers kill thousands through their side-
stream smoke; drunken car drivers kill hundreds of thousands.
And yet approximately 20,000,000 Americans use cannabis –
which is illegal – but no one has yet died from it. In America
around 500,000 people use heroin regularly and another 500,000
use cocaine every day but the total number of deaths attributed
to *all* illegal drugs is around 3,500 a year – and most of those
deaths are a consequence of the fact that the drugs involved are
provided illegally, are often contaminated and are of doubtful
and variable purity. The startling truth is that the illegal drugs
of addiction are not as dangerous as the legal drugs of addiction.

The cruelest irony of all is, perhaps, the fact that drug
dependence and drug injury are now the commonest doctor-
induced diseases and both are among the commonest of all
diseases. At any one time, six out of ten people will be taking a
drug of some kind and half of those drugs will be have been
prescribed by a doctor. If all those drugs were essential and safe
the figures would not be so worrying. But four out of every ten
people who take prescribed drugs suffer severe or noticeable
side effects and many end up needing medical treatment for
problems produced by the drugs they have been given. Every
year in Britain 200,000 people are admitted to hospital because
of a drugs overdose of some kind and 4,000 of them will die. In

other words more people in Britain are killed by prescribed drugs than are killed by illegal drugs in America and Britain together. Amazingly, one in every six people in hospital are there because they have suffered side effects from treatment they have been given. It is, it seems, doctors as much as patients who are addicted to drugs (though it is, of course, patients who end up suffering the physical and mental agonies of that addiction).

In Britain, where doctors get most of their training and information about drugs from drug companies, eight out of ten consultations end with the doctor writing out a prescription. Doctors sometimes claim that this happens because patients expect a prescription (in much the same way that a child visiting Father Christmas in a store grotto expects to be given a present) but this simply is not true. Millions of the patients who are given a prescription did not want to be given drugs and as many as one in seven fail to have their prescriptions dispensed.

Of all the problems produced by the drugs that doctors prescribe, drug addiction is undoubtedly one of the most troublesome. And although doctors have been instrumental in building up the world's heroin and morphine addiction problems, it is with the so-called 'minor' tranquillizers and sedatives that doctors have done most damage. At the start of the twentieth century doctors regularly prescribed bromide for nervous or anxious patients. Thousands became addicted. During the middle part of the century bromide was replaced by the barbiturates which were regarded as much safer and less likely to produce dependence of any kind. Then, in the 1960s and 1970s when the dangers associated with the barbiturates had become widely known, a newly discovered group of drugs – the benzodiazepines – were introduced as safe, effective and non-addictive alternatives for patients who needed help to relax or to get to sleep. Within a very short space of time thousands of doctors were prescribing vast quantities of the benzodiazepines for millions of patients and by the late 1980s virtually every developed country in the world had a major benzodiazepine addiction problem. For the third time in less than a century doctors and the drug industry had successfully created and promoted drug addiction.

The Drugs Myth

With all addictions the size of the problem is increased dramatically by the fact that the majority of addicts cause enormous pain and heartache to those around them. Each individual case of addiction acts like a small explosion, involving and destroying wives, husbands, parents, children, brothers, sisters, friends, neighbours, employers and workmates. No one knows how many lives have been ruined by drug use, abuse or addiction but the total number of lives affected must be at least five times as big when those whose lives are indirectly affected are included. How many of us can say that our lives have never been touched by another's addiction? Addicts are squeezed between those selling drugs (aggressive and threatening when the drugs are illegal and subtle, manipulative and insidious when the drugs are legal); the punitive legal system and the harassed, unimaginative and over-pressured medical profession. Friends and relatives are frequently left to try to pick up the pieces of a shattered life themselves and, fired by a mixture of love, guilt, fear and compassion, are left to struggle to deal with social, mental, emotional, spiritual and physical demands for which they have no training and no preparation.

Although drug addiction is now recognized as a major international problem, many people still have a narrow view of what is a 'drug' and what makes an 'addict'. People who happily drink themselves silly every Saturday night or who smoke sixty cigarettes a day look down their noses at individuals who use cocaine or heroin and imagine that because one type of addiction is legal and another is illegal there must be some real difference between the severity of the two. The truth is, of course, that the only differences are social and legal. The alcohol addict is just as much a victim as the heroin addict and is, indeed, almost certainly more at risk of suffering long-term physiological damage. Social and environmental circumstances and many factors outside individual control (including luck or a lack of it) determine the nature of an individual's addiction.

Sadly and perversely, our attitudes and prejudices are determined by our circumstances, social position, personal experiences, family and, most of all, by our local laws and customs. In the Andes a hill worker will chew coca leaves; in Jamaica a labourer will depend upon cannabis; in New York, London and

Sydney a labourer will rely on beer to get him through the day whereas an officer worker will ease away tensions with a glass or two of vodka or gin. The influence of our laws on our habits is immense and I have no doubt that by making drugs such as heroin, cocaine and marijuana illegal and allowing drugs such as tobacco and alcohol to remain legal the authorities in many countries have helped to contribute to the size of their drug addiction problems. Some folk fear cocaine and heroin because they (wrongly) assume that their very illegality proves that these drugs are dangerous. But they assume that drugs such as alcohol and tobacco which are legal cannot possibly be all that bad. The result is that our bizarre and irrational legislation is responsible for millions of premature deaths. Patterns of drug use – and abuse – are embedded deep in our culture and there is no readily accepted, legally approved drug available anywhere in the world that is not now, has not been in the past, or is not likely to be in the future, the subject of a vigorous campaign of suppression in another culture.

A number of useless and purely pedantic arguments have confused the picture even more and have contributed to the size of our current problem by encouraging a false sense of security among politicians, doctors and drug users. There have, for example, been attempts to divide drugs into 'hard' and 'soft' categories. Drugs such as heroin and cocaine are usually put into the first group whereas drugs such as the benzodiazepines inevitably find themselves in the second group. This sort of classification has no basis in science, for the benzodiazepine tranquillizers are much more dangerous and much more addictive than the so called 'hard' drugs.

There have also been numerous attempts made to differentiate between 'dependence', 'habituation' and 'addiction'. For many years, for example, the amphetamines were regarded as producing nothing more than a mild habituation. It was argued that they could not possibly be considered 'addictive' and the suggestion was that there was a major difference between habituation (a self-directed enthusiasm for a drug) and addiction or dependency (a physiologically based need to keep taking a drug). By the time doctors had realized that the amphetamines are, in fact, among the most addictive of all drugs it was too late: they had been widely over-prescribed and many hundreds of thousands of users had become dangerously and in some cases irreversibly addicted. Today, we know that it is in practical terms quite impossible to differentiate between psychological addiction and physical addiction; both are serious and potentially destructive.

Another major error made by many of those who have written about addiction has been to assume that it is possible to define a particular drug's addictive qualities in a very specific way. In practice this has added to the confusion because it is not solely the pharmacological properties of a drug that make it addictive; it is a combination of the drug's pharmacological qualities and the circumstances in which a person finds and uses the drug. You only have to look at the different effects that alcohol can have on different people to see the truth of this.

And finally the whole picture has been blurred even further by the fact that modern pharmacists have succeeded in producing an almost infinite variety of refinements on original products. Many of these refined products have completely different properties to the originals. Heroin is obtained from opium but is considerably more powerful. Cocaine is derived from the coca leaf but the two substances have very different qualities. By and large the more modern variations are far more powerful and potentially dangerous than the natural originals.

A growing problem

However far back in history you go, there is always evidence to show that whenever times were hard or difficult men and women tried to forget their personal agonies and overcame their fears and anxieties by using drugs. Drug use – and drug abuse – is not a new phenomenon. But it is becoming a bigger problem. And there are several reasons for this.

First, as I have already explained, modern pharmacological compounds are infinitely more complex and more dangerous than original, natural products. We have access to far more potentially addictive products than any other people in history. Today the individual under pressure can choose between heavily promoted and cleverly marketed legal drugs such as tobacco, alcohol, caffeine and tranquillizers and widely available, seemingly glamorous illegal products such as cocaine, heroin and cannabis. People have always used substances such as leaves, fermented grapes, plant juices and hallucinogenic fungi to enliven or calm their lives but never before have there been so many people refining, preparing, manufacturing, distributing and promoting products designed to help us escape from our own world.

Our ability to move around the world in hours instead of months has meant that we now have the opportunity to share habits and customs with different races. We frequently find ourselves in possession of drugs for which we have no historical cultural uses. Every country has its own accepted drugs of addiction (often used for stimulating thought or conversation or for helping people to work or to relax) but international travel has given us open access to a lending library of psychoactive substances which we don't understand or know how to use properly. For centuries the natives of Peru used coca leaves and learned how best to use them. Then scientists from the west took the leaves into their laboratories and produced cocaine. The Peruvians are now using cocaine. We in turn have introduced much of the world to the dangers of the cigarette (the most efficient way of using tobacco to cause cancer) and refined alcohol (the quickest way to rot your liver).

Second, attempts to control drug use by introducing a web of laws have backfired. Many of today's problems have been created by our attempts to outlaw drug use.

Third, we have changed our world enormously in the last century or so in a thousand different ways. Agriculture, industry, communications, transport and welfare – all have changed. In many countries the sanctity of the family has been abolished. Individual pressures in the 'developed' world are quite different today to the pressures which existed a generation ago. Most of us have fewer fundamental fears ('What will we eat?', 'How will we keep warm?') than our ancestors had but we are exposed to far more frustrations and far more pressures which are totally outside our control. Most importantly, the changes have taken place at such a rapid rate that we simply have not been able to evolve fast enough. As a result we have acquired an infinitely varied number of physical and mental problems produced by our responses to the stresses created by these developments.

At the same time that international travel has made it easy for us to exchange drug use with other countries, the variations in local laws and customs have created great confusion and bitterness between many populations. We in the west complain angrily about farmers in South America or the Middle East growing opium poppies or coca bushes and we insist that they destroy their natural, long established crops to protect our citizens from the refined products which our scientists will make out of those simple, natural and relatively harmless substances. At the same time we use drugs such as alcohol which they abhor, condemn and fear. We are so arrogant that when we are told that we must not take our alcohol into their countries we regard them as interfering and we treat their laws with contempt, making no secret of the fact that we think them rather backward and exceptionally repressive.

As a community our attempts to deal with drug addiction have been unsympathetic, ineffective and largely counterproductive. Legislation has been introduced to outlaw those types of addiction which are not protected by powerful business interests, while those drugs which are protected by industry remain freely available and attempts to control their availability or promotion are regarded as unacceptably repressive in a free society. We describe those who use legal drugs as 'sick' and 'in need of help' but those individuals who are caught using illegal drugs get very little sympathy or help. The standard theory seems to be that if an addict is caught he or she must be punished and put in prison. We ignore the fact that this 'remedy' doesn't work because as soon as the addict is released from prison he goes straight back to his old surroundings. The forces and pressures which led him into drug addiction won't have changed (indeed, being in prison has probably made things worse) so his responses to the world won't have changed either. Nothing will have been done to change his self-image, motivation or lifestyle. He picks up his bad habits again not because he has a continuing and irresistible physical need but through social circumstances. Most heroin addicts are not hooked on heroin but they are irretrievably bound to the heroin lifestyle. Sending addicts to prison simply ensures that the problem will continue.

Ever since humans first discovered ways to 'escape' from their misery by the use of drugs, men and women have used artificial stimulants and psychoactive drugs to improve or hide the way they feel. Drug addiction is commoner today than it has ever been. We have spent a fortune trying to suppress drug use. But drug addiction is a plague which is growing faster than at any previous time. Those who sell drugs are richer than ever and drug law enforcement has failed miserably. Drug treatment programmes fail and seem doomed to continue to fail. What all the legislators and politicians and doctors seem to forget is that it is our nature to escape from unhappiness when we can Attempts to prevent or penalize drug use are all doomed to failure.

A more liberal approach

When I first supported the idea of the decriminalization of drugs in 1986, numerous interviewers and reviewers seemed to have difficulty in realizing that I was being serious. Today, the idea has attracted a considerable amount of support. But many of those who opposed decriminalization still refuse even to talk about the idea. Many of those who oppose drug use seem to me to be able to combine hysteria and remarkable naivety with their demands for more legislation, not less. Writing in *The Economist* recently, a worried American citizen argued that 'The solution is a tough-minded policy that identifies and punishes drug use in five areas: at school, behind the wheels of vehicles, for parolees and probationers and for teenagers at home. Such a wide policy of zero tolerance can be enforced only by widespread use of urine testing. When this new technology is employed, the demand for drugs will wane, the gangsters will drop drug sales, and the epidemic will end.' Others worry that any move towards decriminalization will be seen as being 'soft' on crime. Politicians find such an approach difficult to accept, even though their much loved out-and-out war on drug use has clearly failed to have any effect at all.

The Drugs Myth

When an advisory committee suggested in 1968 that Britain should consider changing the law on marijuana, the then Home Secretary James Callaghan said that 'to reduce the penalties for possession, sale or supply of cannabis would be bound to lead people to think that the government takes a less serious view of the effect of drug taking.' In 1972 Richard Nixon set up the National Commission on Marijuana and Drug Abuse in America. The commission recommended the decriminalization of marijuana but Nixon had apparently already rejected the recommendation before the commission had finished its deliberations. When in 1983 it got wind of suggestions that a more liberal attitude towards drug use might prove profitable the United Nations Narcotics Control Board stated that 'determination may sometimes be giving way to permissiveness. To adopt such an attitude would be retrogressive.'

Those who oppose a more liberal approach invariably seem to confuse decriminalization with legalization (the former suggests merely an absence of legal control whereas the latter suggests approval) and to assume that those who support a more liberal approach must be permissive. In fact, of course, decriminalization is usually offered simply as a logical and sane method of controlling and limiting drug abuse more efficiently and humanely. Sometimes those who oppose a more liberal approach do so because they seem genuinely frightened (frequently claiming that drug addicts are a major source of crime and infection in our society and seemingly convinced that anyone who takes one puff on a marijuana cigarette will inevitably end up turning into a super-sex-crazed-child-molesting-old-lady-mugging-bank-robbing-lunatic) while sometimes there is an undeniably racist element in scare propaganda.

When American reporter P. J. O'Rourke suggested legalizing drugs to a policeman, the law enforcement officer replied:'We're talking scum here. Air should be illegal if they breathe it'. According to *The Times* in London, the Guardian Angels' method of dealing with drug offenders in America is 'to raid a house, beat up the addicts and destroy all drugs and equipment; then to empty their pockets and burn their money. It works and costs nothing'.

Even today many voices of the establishment find the mere thought of decriminalization too much to bear. Just look at the attitudes expressed by four of Britain's leading national newspapers in 1989 after I produced a pamphlet entitled *Drugs: The argument for decriminalization*. *The Observer* described suggestions of legalizing drugs as 'nonsense of a pernicious kind'; *The Times* said that 'Drugs are an evil to be fought, not to be accommodated'; *The Guardian* predicted that 'legalizing the trade would only increase addiction', and *The Daily Telegraph* argued pompously that 'a government which gratuitously added one more health risk in order to ease its task would forfeit public respect'. Under continuing pressure from public opinion, politicians all over the western world continue to call for more funds and more resources to fight the drug 'war'.

Maybe our politicians would do better to look at the reasons why people take drugs rather than putting all their efforts into trying to deal with what is a consequence of society's problems rather than a primary problem in itself. We live in a strange society. Our politicians and legislators attack drug use and then go home and drink themselves silly. They give out pompous and patronizing advice and ignore the real problems. In the summer of 1983 the British government issued a press release designed to discourage glue sniffing. The release said: 'Don't do it. It's just not worth it'. The politicians seem to have ignored the fact that when twelve-year-old children are so miserable and lonely and empty of hope and so full of despair that they spend their free hours huddled underneath canal bridges trying to blow their minds and escape the real world by sniffing glue out of old crisp bags, there is something drastically wrong – and an appeal to 'pull up your socks and be a sensible fellow' may not be the sort of help that is needed.

2 | Why prohibition fails

History shows that drug use is an old-established method of dealing with unpleasant stresses and with anxieties of all kinds.

Men and women have always used drugs to enable them to escape from their day-to-day anxieties and worries, to enable them to find peace and temporary contentment, to excite and stimulate themselves when they feel bored, to give themselves energy when they feel tired and to allow themselves to experience and explore new worlds.

Primitive peoples chewed nuts and leaves and ate mushrooms to give themselves energy; the priests of ancient civilizations used herbs to enable them to influence the moods of their congregations and to enter mystical states in which they could talk to the Gods; opium was first used seven thousand years ago; alcohol was first brewed and sold five thousand years ago. The use of drugs to change perceptions is older than industry, older than the law, older than medicine and older than farming. In ancient caves archaeologists have discovered evidence to show that stone age people heated poppy heads so that they could inhale the fumes in order to forget the cold, their hunger and their fear of being eaten alive.

Every generation – even those from times which now seem to us austere and obsessed with strictly regimenting the behaviour of the masses – used drugs to escape from those things

16

which they found distasteful, distressing or simply disappointing. No group of individuals were more correct than the British Victorians but it is clear that they were avid drug users. Alcohol was popular but the most widely abused drug of the age was laudanum – a tincture of opium – which was immensely popular with men and women of every social group. Everyone from the aristocracy and the intelligentsia down to the working classes consumed their laudanum in a seemingly endless variety of over-the-counter preparations such as Godfrey's Cordial and Dr J. Collis Browne's Chlorodyne. Addicts drank a pint or even more a day of their favourite, powerful concoction. Writers such as Edgar Allan Poe, Charles Dickens, Wilkie Collins, and Thomas de Quincey all wrote under the influence of opium while Robert Louis Stephenson wrote *The Strange Case of Dr Jekyll and Mr Hyde* under the influence of cocaine and Sir Arthur Conan Doyle used the same drug when working on his Sherlock Holmes stories. Not to be outdone, the Americans of this era took to drug use with great vigour and by the end of the nineteenth century could choose from over fifty thousand over-the-counter medicines which contained drugs such as heroin, morphine, cocaine and cannabis. It was even possible to buy products containing opium through the Sears Roebuck mail order catalogue.

Ever since the first bureaucrat discovered the pleasures of obfuscation, authorities of one sort or another have attempted to stop the use of drugs. In the Ottoman Empire Sultan Murad IV introduced the death penalty for smoking. In the seventeenth century tobacco was prohibited in several European countries and a Russian Tsar introduced a law ruling that anyone possessing tobacco should be tortured until he revealed the name of his dealer. In Germany the death penalty was introduced for tobacco users in 1691. But every available piece of evidence shows quite clearly that all attempts to stop the use of drugs have been unfailingly ineffective. If history shows anything at all, then it shows that it will never be possible to outlaw illegal drug use because no law can ever make the demand disappear; and so long as there is a demand for drugs there will be people willing to supply the required product or something similar to it. Laws which are designed to outlaw drug use are doomed even more certainly than the laws which

The Drugs Myth

are destined to outlaw prostitution. The prostitute's client is likely to be respectable and to fear exposure but the client of the illegal drug salesman will often live outside the system and may in any case be well aware that there is little social disapproval among his peers of drug use and abuse.

Indeed, if drug laws have any effect on drug users it is to excite them rather than to discourage them. Many of those who use drugs do so because their lives are dull; they are looking for stimulation. What those who call for more laws do not understand is that the risk of being caught frequently increases the pleasure of drug use and attracts and encourages the drug user, and that the demand for drugs which provide some relief from life's vicissitudes is deeply engrained. In a crisis people will use almost anything to help them escape from their world. In the mid-nineteenth century the distillation of illicit whisky in Ireland fell off partly because of the failure of the corn crop and partly because of the legendary activities of the temperance campaign led by Father Mathew – a miracle worker who is personally credited with having managed to persuade half a million Irishmen to take the pledge. But just because the Irish were not drinking alcohol, they did not stop drugging themselves. While the stills remained unused the Irish started using a replacement. The drug was readily available because it was at the time being (quite wrongly) used by doctors as a treatment for cholera and it was popular because it produced a form of intoxication which was similar to that associated with alcohol. Within a very small space of time 50,000 Ulstermen and women had consumed 17,000 gallons of ether as an 'alternative' social lubricant. The popularity of ether dropped suddenly when the following year's successful grain crop enabled the illegal still owners to get back to business and start making whiskey again. The pledges offered to Father Mathew were conveniently forgotten.

The American attempt to outlaw the sale and use of alcohol during the 1920s illustrates perfectly the uselessness of legislation as a weapon in the war to control drug abuse. Prohibition began in 1919 as a result of the Volstead Act which was passed as the eighteenth amendment to the United States constitution after pressure from organizations such as the Women's Christian Temperance Movement – but despite a veto from the

18

American president. In an attempt to ensure that the new law was obeyed and that no one made, sold or drank any alcohol at all, over a thousand special agents were hired and equipped with special badges, pistols, machine guns and hand grenades. Despite the enthusiastic publicity films which showed special agents making holes in barrels of illicit whisky and gin and allowing the contents to spill down into the drains, the result of prohibition was a disaster of quite monumental proportions.

By making the manufacture and sale of alcohol illegal the government closed down respectable distilleries and bars and opened the way for crooks like Al Capone to take over and supply the continuing demand for alcohol. By the mid 1920s – just half a dozen years after prohibition had been introduced – there were 30,000 illegal clubs selling alcohol in New York alone, while Al Capone controlled over 10,000 bars in Chicago. The government had opened the way for the development of a massive, powerful, well structured and extraordinarily rich underworld. By 1933 when the government realized that prohibition was just not going to work, America had acquired an enormous underground network of well organized criminals.

When, after fourteen years of prohibition, the American government finally realized that the consumption of alcohol was almost certainly going up rather than coming down, they passed the twenty-first amendment to the constitution, re-pealed the prohibition laws and allowed the legal sale of alcohol once again. But prohibition had already done more harm than good. In the first two years of prohibition the number of hospital admissions from alcoholism decreased slightly but within three years the incidence of alcoholism had gone up to pre-prohibition levels. After prohibition ended the amount of alcohol being produced and consumed *fell* by an astonishing fifty per cent.

More important still, in order to maintain their lavish lifestyles and keep their armies occupied the crooks who had made their fortune out of alcohol had to look for something else to sell. No one should have been surprised when the mobsters started importing and selling drugs such as heroin and cocaine. The prohibition of alcohol was a major social disaster which encouraged thousands of people to take up drinking (its very illegality made it exciting and glamorous and the gangsters selling it were clever enough to make their clubs fashionable and attractive places) and also created the crime empire which now imports, distributes and markets narcotics. The international drugs 'industry' which currently inspires so much legislation around the world is largely a consequence of the legal attempt to end the consumption of alcohol.

Those politicians who want to see the prohibition of heroin and cocaine enforced by the law seem conveniently to have forgotten the lessons they should have learned from prohibition. They should listen to the wisdom of John D. Rockefeller Junior who was originally in favour of prohibition but who, having seen the eighteenth amendment working, admitted 'that a vast array of lawbreakers has been recruited and financed on a colossal scale; that many of our best citizens, piqued at what they regarded as an infringement of their private rights, have openly and unabashedly disregarded the eighteenth amendment; that, as an inevitable result, respect for all law has been greatly lessened; that crime has increased to an unprecedented degree – all this I have slowly and reluctantly come to believe'.

When prohibition ended, and alcohol was again legalized, a government that had one day opposed the drinking of alcohol with all its might immediately started taking a tax on sales of alcohol. This apparent oddity illustrates quite nicely the hypocrisy which is never far from the surface when drugs are concerned.

Consider, for example, what happened in China in the nineteenth century.

In the eighteenth century the Portuguese had started selling opium to the Chinese. When they realized the commercial potential the British started cultivating huge opium plantations in India where they could grow the opium they intended to sell to the Chinese. The sale of opium to China soon became a major source of income for Britain and for companies such as Jardine Matheson of Hong Kong and by the 1830s British companies were exporting half a million pounds of opium to China every year. When the Chinese emperor became worried about the effect all this opium was having on his people, he tried to stop the trade, but the British started a war to force the Chinese to allow them to continue selling the drug. The opium wars dominated much of the middle period of the nineteenth century simply because it was in Britain's commercial interest to maintain its drug sales. Many of Britain's largest international companies founded their fortunes on the sale of a drug which is now illegal.

How, I wonder, would Britain like it now if the Colombians began a war to protect their cocaine trade? Is it possible that the descendants and beneficiaries of the gangsters who currently sell cocaine and heroin will be running respectable and politically powerful international companies in the mid twenty-first century?

3 | Toxic stress

Why the drug problem is getting worse.
Why twentieth-century life puts people
under so much pressure that they need to
use drugs to survive. And why those who
endorse our drug control laws are
hypocrites.

Despite all the efforts that have been made to combat drug use
and to limit drug abuse, there is absolutely no doubt that drug
use and drug abuse are both increasing rapidly.

In theory we should live relatively stress-free lives. Few of
us in the west have to worry about keeping warm, having
enough food to keep us alive or finding somewhere warm and
secure to sleep at night. We are better equipped with gadgets
designed to make our lives easy than any of our ancestors ever
were. We *should* be happy. We should not need to take drugs to
find contentment or to help us escape from the world in which
we live. We should not need to use drugs in order to make our
lives more exciting.

But more and more people do take drugs. And millions of
perfectly normal, apparently sensible, outwardly successful
men and women are prepared to risk their freedom and their
health for the relatively short moments of pleasure and contentment which they obtain from using drugs.

There are many reasons why.

Some people use drugs to help them cope with daily life;
some want to numb their minds; some want to forget things
that they cannot otherwise forget; some need drugs to help
them cope with the frustrations they encounter every day.
Boredom, emptiness, alienation, loneliness, anxiety and depression – these are just a few of the reasons why drug abuse is
endemic in our apparently rich and successful society.

The truth is that we live in strange, difficult and confusing times. In material ways we are richer than any of our ancestors. But in spiritual ways we are infinitely poorer.

Most of us live in well equipped homes that our great-grandparents would marvel at. We have access to (relatively) clean drinking water at the turn of a tap. We can obtain light to work by and heat to cook by at the flick of a switch. Our homes are stuffed with possessions. We have wall-to-wall fitted carpets, automatic ovens, washing machines, tumble driers, dish washers, food blenders, vacuum cleaners, television sets, video recorders and a whole host of other devices designed either to make our working hours easier or our leisure hours more enjoyable. If we want to travel anywhere we can climb into our own motor cars or we can use public buses, trains or aeroplanes. We are surrounded by the gaudy signs of our wealth and the physical consequences of several thousand years of human ambition and endeavour.

But despite all this, loneliness, unhappiness, anxiety and depression are now commoner than at any other time in our history. There has never before been as much sadness, dissatisfaction and frustration as there is today. We have become so dependent upon the 'things' with which we have surrounded ourselves that when they break down we become aggressive and irritable. We cannot cope without them. The demand for drug-based solutions to our problems has multiplied apparently endlessly.

We have access to sophisticated communications systems and yet never before have we been so aware of our ignorance and never before have so many people felt so lonely. We can fire messages around the world at the touch of a button but we no longer talk to one another. We have more power over our environment than our ancestors ever dreamt of and yet we are regularly and bitterly reminded of our helplessness and our vulnerability. We are materially wealthy and yet spiritually deprived. We have conquered our planet and begun to conquer space and yet we are continually reminded of our woeful inability to look after the planet we live on or to live in peace with one another.

On the face of it, twentieth-century life doesn't look as though it ought to provide us with too much pressure. From the point of view of our ancestors, or indeed of the millions of less fortunate individuals living in less well developed parts of the world, we have few basic worries. Yet, there is little doubt that we suffer far more from stress than our ancestors ever did. Stress is endemic in our society and our use of and dependence on drugs is just one consequence of our inability to cope with the stresses which we have created for ourselves.

The fundamental reason why we suffer so much from stress these days is that our bodies were designed a long, long time ago and are ill suited for modern society. We were designed for the sort of instant world in which there is always likely to be a sabre-toothed tiger waiting just around the corner. And we were designed very well for circumstances like that.

Today, if we are faced with a sudden emergency our bodies respond quickly, dramatically and logically. Our muscles tighten, our hearts beat faster, our blood pressure goes up, adrenalin surges through our arteries, acid pours into our stomachs and our bodies are put on immediate alert. All these physiological changes are designed to help us survive the encounter. They help us fight, run, jump and climb with unusual and quite exceptional agility. The faster heart beat ensures that as much blood as possible reaches our muscles so that they receive a plentiful supply of oxygen. The rise in blood pressure has a similar purpose. The acid pouring into our stomachs ensures that any food that is there will be converted into usable energy, speedily and efficiently.

These basic traits were handed down from generation to generation for the very good reason that anyone who did not respond in this instantaneous way would not survive. Individuals who were not able to run, jump, climb or fight well were eaten up by man-eating marauding tigers. Individuals who did respond in an immediate way lived to produce and raise the next generation. Simple genetics have meant that through ordinary selection processes we are these days particularly well adapted for a world full of dangerous animals and immediate physical dangers.

Unfortunately, these natural, automatic responses are no longer appropriate. Indeed, they are a hindrance rather than a help, for we have changed our world far more rapidly than our bodies have been able to evolve. Instead of being faced with a tiger, a pack of hungry wolves or an angry bear we are far more likely to find ourselves having to face unemployment, large fuel bills or officious policemen. None of these modern problems is easily solved. None can be dealt with by a faster heart beat, a higher blood pressure or tense muscles.

Never before in history have there been such dramatic changes. Attitudes, fashions, fears, feelings and ambitions have all altered rapidly. Revolutionary changes in navigation, medicine, science, military tactics, agriculture, industry and so on have all changed the world a great deal. But our bodies are much the same as they were several thousand years ago. It takes thousands – millions – of years for the human body to adapt and we have moved far too quickly for our own good. Today our protective physical responses are sadly inappropriate. When we find ourselves facing huge bills that we cannot pay; legal threats that we cannot cope with; unemployment caused by factors totally outside our control; officialdom that is backed by authority without being restricted by responsibility; or even the simple need to find a car parking space, we still respond in the simple, physical way: our muscles become tense and our hearts beat faster. But responses designed for a physical threat are of absolutely no help in our world. Indeed, these traditional physical responses are doubly inappropriate, for our modern problems tend to continue for such long periods of time that a dramatic physical response can become positively harmful rather than merely inappropriate. For example, if you are worried about inflation and possible unemployment, then your blood pressure will go up and your heart will beat faster for as long as your worries continue. Since that could well turn out to be months or even years, it is not difficult to see how the damage gets done.

The consequences of all this stress vary enormously. Doctors now agree that nine out of ten physical symptoms are directly caused by stress or else made worse by it. And the massive incidence of anxiety, nervousness, depression and sleeplessness is, without a doubt, a direct consequence of our exposure to, and our inability to cope with, stress. It is hardly surprising that millions of people try to escape from their stresses with the aid of drugs, though the precise type of drug that a sufferer uses will depend very much on the nature of the environment in which he lives and on the people with whom he most commonly spends his time. An international film star may turn to cocaine; a miner to beer and cigarettes; a housewife to one of the widely prescribed benzodiazepines. The type of drug chosen will depend to a large extent on local traditions and expectations. In the east the traditional way of dealing with pressure is to dampen down responses to stress and opium and heroin are both particularly well suited to this because they both make the user feel calm, satisfied and contented. Drives, demands, expectations and ambitions are effectively removed. In the west, however, people feel that they have to keep going and to stay aggressive. And alcohol, which removes the inhibitions, is a much more suitable drug for that sort of response.

As we become materially richer and more powerful so we seem to become spiritually more deprived and individually more afraid. The more we acquire, the more we seem to need; and the more we learn, the more we seem condemned by our ignorance. The more control we have over our environment, the more damage we do to it and to ourselves. The more successful we become in financial terms, the more we seem determined to destroy the qualities and virtues which lead to happiness and contentment. The more we learn about other worlds, the more we seem to forget about our private duties and responsibilities to one another.

As manufacturers and advertizers have skilfully and deliberately translated our wants into needs, so we have exchanged generosity and caring for greed and self-concern. Politicians, teachers, parents and scientists have encouraged each succeeding generation to convert simple dreams and aspirations into fiery no-holds-barred ambitions. In the name of progress we have sacrificed common sense, goodwill and thoughtfulness and the gentle, the weak and the warm-hearted have been trampled upon by hordes of embittered victims who have been taught to think only of the future and never of the present or the past. The society in our global village is a sad one; the cornerstones of our modern world are selfishness, greed, anger and hatred. Too few people talk, listen or help one another. The family unit has been shattered by progress. The driving forces we are taught to respect are greed and ambition.

Toxic stress

During the last fifty years or so we have changed our world almost beyond recognition. Advertizing agencies, television producers and newspaper editors have given us new aims to strive for, new hopes, new ambitions and new aspirations. At the same time they have also given us new fears and new anxieties. With the aid of psychologists clever advertizing copywriters have learned to exploit our weaknesses and our natural apprehensions. The advertizers have created ever expanding demands for new and increasingly expensive but worthless products. Our world has been turned upside down. Values and virtues have been turned inside out. Tradition, dignity and craftsmanship have been pushed aside in the constant search for greater profitability.

Our exposure to a type of stress that I call *toxic* begins at a very early age: it begins in earnest the moment we attend school for the first time. We are taught to take education seriously but we are not told the price we will have to pay. To understand the potential costs to the human spirit and soul it is first necessary to understand the purpose of the education that society is offering. Society does not want to educate people so that they become more thoughtful, more creative or wiser. What would be the point of that? Society doesn't want people to broaden their horizons or enhance their vision. Society doesn't want to instil passion (that can be troublesome and inconvenient) and it doesn't want people to think for themselves (that can be costly and disruptive). What society wants is obedience. Society – the social structure which we have created but which has now acquired a strength and a force of its own – values obedience highly and rewards the obedient more than any other group. Society knows that the obedient will work hard without question. Society knows that the obedient can be relied upon to do work that is dull, repetitive and possibly even dangerous. Society knows that the obedient are unlikely to be troubled by spiritual or moral fears. Society knows that the obedient will fit neatly into whatever hierarchy may exist and will put loyalty above honesty and integrity. Society will always reward those who are obedient because society wants to show other people the value of obedience. If you become obedient then you will also become a good and reliable customer; you will buy things that you don't really need; you will accept shoddy workmanship and unreliability without complaint; you will accept new fashions as necessary and you will buy new clothes and new cars when society wants you to buy these things rather than when you *need* them. As far as the powerful interests which rule society are concerned, the obedient customer is a passive customer and the passive customer is the best customer. The modern educational system (in its widest sense) is designed to support the structure of our society, but because it inevitably suppresses free thought and encourages the development of frustration it is also a major force in the development of toxic stress. Children, parents and teachers have little or no control over their destiny, which is manipulated for them by the 'system'. Society does not encourage teachers or pupils to think for themselves.

How advertizing causes toxic stress

Even as children we are regarded as consumers and from the moment we can sit in front of a television set companies spend huge amounts of money trying to persuade us to buy their products or services. Every day our custom is solicited in a thousand different ways – some subtle and some crude. Every day we will come face to face with an almost infinite variety of messages and exhortations.

The professionals who prepare the advertizements we see are only too well aware that it is no longer enough for them to tell us the value of the product they are selling. These days the competition is so great that advertizing agencies are no longer content to tell us how to satisfy our basic needs; these days they know that in order to succeed they must create new needs; their advertizing must create wants and desires, hopes and aspirations and then turn those wants, desires, hopes and aspirations into *needs*. They do this through exaggeration and deceit and through the continuing and cynical exploitations of our weaknesses and our fears. Modern advertizing agencies know that it is impossible to sell anything to a satisfied individual. But, in order to keep the money coming in, the agencies must keep encouraging us to buy; they must constantly find new and better ways to sell us stuff we don't want. Any fool can sell us products and services that we need. The trick lies in turning our most ephemeral (and even non-existent) wants into basic needs.

In order to do this, advertizing agencies must use all their professional skills to make us dissatisfied with what we already have. They need us to be constantly dissatisfied and frustrated. They constantly need to create new and more virulent forms of toxic stress.

Modern advertizing raises the intensity of our desires and builds our dissatisfaction and our fears in order to satisfy its own mercenary ends. Modern advertizing is a creative art. The advertizing professional is hired to create unhappiness and dissatisfaction. He is paid to make us want more possessions, excitement or status. He is paid to keep us *dissatisfied*. The ultimate irony is that he is also paid to sell us many of the drugs we need to take to escape from the world into which we have been plunged by our created needs, frustrations and sadnesses.

Advertizing is designed to make us dissatisfied with anything which cannot be profitable. Advertizers want to take away your appreciation of the simple things in life so that they can sell you complicated and expensive things. They would rather you sat down to watch football on television than that you kicked a ball round in the park. They want you to wash away your natural, sexual odours and replace them with odours taken from the sexual glands of animals. They want you to be in such a hurry that you eat instant foods rather than growing and then preparing your own vegetables. They want you to feel a failure if you don't fill your house with the latest gadgets. They don't want you to be able to wear the old clothes you feel comfortable in. They don't want you to be able to walk freely through your town. They don't want you to enjoy any real freedom. They need your money and so they want your soul.

The advertizing industry is responsible for much of the sickness and the unhappiness in our society. Advertizing may suggest that if you buy such-and-such a product you will become popular and successful. But you will be disappointed. Even if you buy the product you will remain frustrated and

dissatisfied. The advertizing professionals make many promises which they know they cannot keep. To the spiritual and
mental frustration created by all this disappointment you must
add physical frustration too, for the chances are high that the
product you buy will soon fail. Obsolescence is built-in and
essential to all new products. Built-in mechanical or fashionable obsolescence enables the car companies to keep making
and selling us new cars which we cannot easily afford and do
not really need. The advertizing professionals do not care about
the poor, the disabled, the sick, the frail or the unemployed –
these people have no money and do not matter, so modern
advertizing destroys them. It shows them things they cannot
have, and services they cannot buy. It inflames their desires,
creates wants and then turns those wants into needs, thereby
creating frustration and passion – and violence. The poor do not
even have the simple satisfaction of discovering that the products they are offered are never likely to satisfy the promises
made for them! Advertizing is one of the greatest causes of toxic
stress. Advertizing is built on promises that can never be kept
and is a major cause of drug use and drug abuse. Advertizing
succeeds by making people unhappy; it represents false temp-
tations, hollow hopes, unhappiness and disenchantment; it
inspires values which are based on fear, greed and avarice.

It is hardly surprising that all these pressures have produced new stresses and strains of their own. The pressure to
succeed joins with the pressure to conform and the pressure to
acquire; as a result we live in a world where the basic levels of
stress are fixed at dangerously high levels. Each one of us is
confronted with massive amounts of stress every day of our
lives. Many of the stresses we are faced with at work and at
home can be controlled or avoided. But the stresses which are
an inherent part of the world around us – stresses which
produce difficult to define frustrations – produce bitterness and
a deep sense of ill-defined, unexplained, inexplicable despair. I
call these stresses 'toxic' because they produce a deep sense of
frustration and unhappiness; the more thoughtful and imag-
inative an individual is, the more likely he or she is to become a
victim.

The sensitive and intelligent respond to toxic stress by
becoming unhappy and confused. She feels that she ought to be

doing more with her life. He feels that control of his life is slipping away from him. She suffers from a range of symptoms and ailments for which there never seems to be any completely satisfactory treatment. He feels nervous or anxious even though he knows that he doesn't have anything to be nervous about. She feels strangely and inexplicably alone. He feels constantly rushed, unable to find the time to do all the things he feels he ought to do, let alone the things that he would like to do. She worries unreasonably about quite trivial insignificant things that in her heart she knows don't really matter. He feels constantly tired, listless and short of energy. She feels an almost overwhelming and irresistible urge to run away from everything. He feels that life is not as much fun as it used to be – or should be. She feels a complete sense of despair about the future of the world.

The need to start taking drugs is almost entirely a consequence of dissatisfaction and inadequacies, both of which our society deliberately breeds. People are led to believe that life owes them more and more (always more than they have – however much that may be); advertizing encourages them to feel resentment, frustration and envy. Individuals who are filled with fear and despair are easy game for those who 'sell' solutions; too late they discover that drugs of whatever kind are no real answer, no real solution; they provide a temporary means of escape but nothing more substantial than that.

Although most developed countries now have some regulations governing the amount or type of advertizing that can be used to promote alcohol and tobacco, the big international companies are extremely adept at getting their message across despite the regulations. And there is no doubt that advertizing – however subtle – is extremely effective. For example, in a report published in the *Health Education Journal* in 1984, Frank Ledwith, research fellow in the department of education at the University of Manchester, reported on a survey which involved 880 secondary school children. Ledwith found that the children he questioned were most aware of those cigarette brands which were most frequently associated with sponsored sports events on television. By testing to see how many children recognized the name of a tobacco company before and after a sponsored snooker competition appeared on television, the research showed that sponsorship of a sport that is going to appear on television acts as very effective cigarette advertizing and gets round the modest legislation in Britain which is, theoretically at least, designed to outlaw television advertizing of tobacco.

There is, indeed, a massive advantage in advertizing a product by associating it with a sport. The people who watch the programmes and see the brand name on television quickly come to associate the name of the product with their sporting heroes. This gives the product glamour and status. There is no doubt that by sponsoring a sporting event a tobacco company can implant its product's name in the minds of young viewers (and they, after all, are the customers of the future) far more effectively than it could by buying straightforward advertizing space.

A growing number of agencies are now aware that it often pays to plan promotional campaigns in unusual ways to attract customers to a product. One market research firm recommended to a tobacco company that in order to sell its product to young people effectively it should forget about advocating low tar brands and should ignore the health question altogether. Instead the company was advised to relate its advertizing to adult activities such as sex and alcohol or to link its products to illegal activities such as pot smoking. The market researchers recommended this aggressive approach because the evidence suggests that it is easier to persuade children to start smoking by telling them that smoking is bad for them and suggesting that it is illegal than by pointing out that a particular brand has less tar in it and is much safer.

One of the big questions about tobacco and alcohol advertizing concerns the effectiveness of the advertizing in attracting new recruits. Both the tobacco industry and the alcohol industry argue that their advertizing is designed to persuade existing drinkers and smokers to switch brands, rather than to encourage non-smokers or non-drinkers to start smoking and drinking. In a publication called 'The Impact of Advertising on the United Kingdom Alcoholic Drink Market' and published by the Advertising Association in 1983, Dr L.W. Hagan and M.J. Waterson claimed that 'alcohol advertising is virtually entirely specific brand-orientated advertising: it is promoting a particular name of beer or spirits, etc.; it is never promoting alcoholic drink as a total concept'. The authors also claim that 'only a very small fraction of the population can be classed as alcoholics or as abusing alcohol in a serious manner'.

This argument, frequently put forward in a similar way by the tobacco companies, does not stand up well to examination. The fact is that tobacco companies continue to advertize in those countries where they have a sales monopoly and it is extremely difficult to accept that advertizing which shows a man or a woman enjoying a successful or pleasant lifestyle while smoking a cigarette will have no effect on young, uncommitted viewers. I firmly believe that the advertizing of tobacco and of alcohol has had a most powerful effect on the number of people using those two drugs and am appalled at the way in which major, international tobacco and alcohol companies are now enthusiastically promoting their products in underdeveloped and developing countries (using cynical and aggressive marketing techniques that would be banned in much of the world) where there is a considerable envy of the western life style, very little pressure on the authorities to introduce controls or warnings and virtually no understanding among the general population of the hazards associated with these two activities.

The world's major advertizing agencies have helped to create a massive and widespread need for pharmacological support. And, in true cynical style, they have succeeded in satisfying that need by helping to promote two of the world's most dangerous and most addictive drugs. There is a certain absurdity in the fact that, while cocaine and heroin smugglers are hounded and persecuted, the elegant, well educated executives who work for the tobacco industry, the alcohol industry and the advertizing industry receive huge financial rewards and acclaim from society for their destructive and damaging work.

The stress of boredom

The pressure from advertizers is not, of course, the only source of pressure that causes stress and puts people into a situation where they start taking drugs in order to escape from their world. Some of the pressures which lead to drug taking are unsuspected. Boredom, for example, is one of the most underrated sources of pressure in our society. We tend to think of it as being nothing more than a mild, usually temporary nuisance; a fleeting irritation that can be cured with a good book, an interesting conversation or an amusing film. The truth is very different. There is now considerable evidence to show that boredom is a major cause of distress, anxiety and depression.

Many different groups of people suffer from boredom.

There are the millions who are unemployed and who see no prospects of finding employment. In just about every so-called civilized country a growing number of men and women know that they will probably never work again. And while that is bad enough the horrors endured by young school leavers facing a lifetime of unemployment hardly bear thinking about. As factories become more automated and offices become more streamlined there is a smaller and smaller need for factory workers or office staff. And as the number of people gainfully employed in factories and offices falls, so the demand for service industries falls too. For as long as we continue our love affair with computers and high technology we are trapped in this spiral and the levels of unemployment will continue to rise. Because we live in a job-orientated society where status and self-respect depend on having a job with some position and power, unemployment produces a number of very damaging forces. The individual who has lost a job, or who is unable to find a job at all, will undoubtedly feel a tremendous sense of guilt and failure. But there will also be seemingly endless days of dull, unremitting boredom.

Second, there are those whose jobs are simply undemanding, unrewarding and uninspiring. Not so many years ago just about any job required skills of some kind. A craftsman would be expected to have agile fingers and skilful hands. A clerk would be expected to have a facility with words or figures. Today, however, in shops and offices there are millions of employees whose jobs are quite free of skills or responsibilities. There are computers and word processors which can write letters, add up numbers, check spelling and keep files far more efficiently and rapidly than any clerk. In factories, there are countless thousands whose work demands nothing more than that they act as nursemaids to complex pieces of machinery which can turn out an endless series of perfect objects, created to standards that no craftsman could ever hope to match. The machines have become the principals in just about all working relationships. And instead of doing work from which they can derive satisfaction and pride, men who might have once been regarded as skilled craftsmen simply baby-sit masses of machinery which deny their operators any opportunity for pride, pleasure or self-expression.

Then there are the men and women who have been encouraged to retire early. Trade union officials routinely and noisily campaign for earlier retirement for their members. And yet millions of people regularly complain that they had to retire too soon. Even the simplest and least demanding job offers something in the way of authority, meaning, purpose, companionship and friendship. A man may complain about his job, his working conditions and his employer but at least he has something positive about which to complain. Even that simple pleasure, that fundamental human delight, is denied the individual who has retired too soon.

Next, there are those children at school who can see no prospect for themselves other than years of collecting unemployment money. For them there can be no bright future, no dreams, and no ambitions to nurture. Their school work becomes unbearably dull because they lose heart and see little point in struggling through academic chores that can lead them nowhere.

Finally, there are those housewives who, perhaps more than any other group in our society, are modern day victims of boredom. They may live in comfortable homes and have healthy, good-looking families dressed in attractive clothes. But their lives are too often planned and organized around pieces of household machinery: washing machines, tumble driers, freezers, microwave ovens and pop-up toasters in relation to which they have no creative role. Their opportunities for self-expression or real fulfilment are slim indeed. The women's liberation movement has reminded them of their rights and of their potential but it has done very little to help them achieve those ambitions.

35

The Drugs Myth

For all these people boredom is a driving force that pushes them relentlessly along a road to one or other of the many forms of addiction – their choice will depend upon their circumstances. The bored housewife may end up taking tranquillizers. The bored school boy starts sniffing glue or, if he lives in an area where heroin use is common, he may become a heroin addict. Other men and women take to tobacco or alcohol.

Boredom remains consistently underestimated as a driving force among addicts. The reality of it all was perhaps best described by William Burroughs in his book *Junkie*. Describing his childhood, Burroughs wrote:

> At this time I was greatly impressed with the autobiography of a burglar called *You Can't Win*. The author claimed to have spent a good part of his life in jail. It sounded good to me compared with the dullness of a Midwest suburb where all contact with life was shut out. You become a narcotics addict because you do not have strong motivations in any other direction. Junk wins by default. I tried it as a matter of curiosity. Most addicts I have talked to report a similar experience. They did not start using drugs for any reason they can remember. They just drifted along until they got hooked.

With boredom behind their need for drugs it is hardly surprising that so many addicts return to drug taking within a year or two of giving up. It is often said that addicts return to their addiction because they cannot stand the uncomfortable symptoms of withdrawal. But that really is not true. The truth is that the depths of boredom are so great that drug addicts take drugs not to ward off withdrawal symptoms but because the modest pleasures afforded by drug taking exceed the pleasures normally available to them.

It has long been established that there is a link between unemployment and depression, and between boredom and the search for risk and excitement provided by drugs. But in recent years it has become clear that in some ways the welfare state itself can be extremely unhealthy, for as it takes away personal responsibility, so it produces a real need for thrills and excitement.

36

Why do people become addicts?

For many years experts around the world have argued about whether or not it is possible to define the type of individual who is most likely to become an addict. It has been suggested that the majority of addicts have personality problems which create social difficulties and that it is these social problems which are eventually responsible for the individual's need to turn to drugs. It has been argued that people who became addicts are invariably shy, sensitive and exceptionally nervous; individuals who are emotionally uncertain and, underneath a veneer of sophistication and strength, in desperate need of love and affection. Potential addicts, it has been said, are people who have difficulty in forming close relationships with other people, people who find that drugs help them by providing them with relief, support or confidence. Drug addicts, it is argued, are lonely and insecure people who derive comfort from the drugs they take.

Other psychologists have argued that addicts are usually inadequate or inferior in some way and need drug support because they find themselves constantly failing to fulfill social expectations. To illustrate their argument they refer to addicts who have turned to drugs when they have been unable to satisfy their parents' ambitions. These people tend to be guilt-ridden, hard working and exceptionally vulnerable to criticism. They have little or no self-confidence and although they may be far more successful than they realise they are often driven by a deep sense of continuing despair and personal failure. They may also feel an unexpressed, even subconscious, sense of anger towards one or both parents.

I have also seen it said that the majority of addicts are rather childish in their outlook, that they tend to be depressives, that their behaviour is often excessive, that they are unusually intelligent and frustrated by their inability to make any head-way in life, that they are disorganized, exceptionally unruly and unable to cope with pressure and that they are, quite simply, over-demanding both of themselves and of society.

All these explanations can, of course, be summed up in one word: immaturity.

The Drugs Myth

If the experts are to be believed, people take drugs because they cannot cope and they cannot cope because they have not become mature enough to deal with life's problems sensibly and dispassionately.

But this is, of course, only a fraction of the story.

Many immature people get through life quite successfully without ever using drugs. And many apparently mature individuals become totally dependent on drug support. The truth is that very few of us could ever claim to be totally in charge of our lives and always capable of coping with problems and pressures in a sensible way. Most of us would admit that under some circumstances we feel nervous or inadequate, incompetent or rebellious. Indeed, responses of that type can be an asset rather than a liability, an enriching factor rather than one likely to damage the quality of our lives. After all, it is uncertainty and insecurity which drive us onwards and upwards and it is vulnerability and rebelliousness which give us our creative faculties.

I do not believe that personality is normally the decisive influence on an individual's chances of becoming a drug addict; it is not so much the personality of the individual which ultimately determines whether or not he becomes an addict but the circumstances in which he finds himself. In these cases, people are always too willing to blame the *victim*.

Addiction is above all culturally based: 72 per cent of the heroin addicts among United States servicemen in Vietnam came off heroin with relative ease once they got home and away from the war and from Vietnam. It was being in Vietnam, fighting a confusing war, which led them to addiction. Given the right circumstances we are all potentially vulnerable; we all have weaknesses and fears; there are times when we all need to escape from pain, hopelessness and isolation. The only factor that separates the addict from the non-addict is the fact that the addict has found himself in a situation where his personality has proved too fragile, while the non-addict has not yet strayed from an environment in which he is able to feel competent and in control. Anyone tempted to feel smug or self-satisfied at not being an addict (and remember that most of us are addicted to *something*) should remember that it is fate which determines our circumstances, our needs and, eventually, our vulnerability. People who become addicts are simply people who have gone too far, who have pushed themselves beyond the limit of their endurance and who need drug support to help them cope with their anger, their shame, their guilt, their isolation and their frustration and, indeed, with life. If the drug is effective then they are likely to become hooked; the stronger the relief the greater the compulsion. Addicts may be weak but they are weak because they have pushed themselves and they have pushed themselves because society has encouraged them to do just that.

The final irony is that we have created a society which breeds addicts. More than that we have created a society which profits from addicts. Back in 1975 American President Gerald Ford seemed to show more than a usual amount of understanding (for a politician) when he said: 'We should stop raising unrealistic expectations of total elimination of drug abuse from or society . . . The sobering fact is that some members of any society will seek escape from the stresses of life through drug use'. What he perhaps should have gone on to say is that legal rules will not define or restrict the drugs which those who need the help of drugs choose to use; the existence of laws means that there will always be some drug users forced to break the law. People become addicts because there are problems in their lives which they cannot solve; the fact that the solution they have chosen eventually creates new problems which mask and overtake in significance the original problems is a social irony.

It is hardly surprising that millions of people have taken to drugs to try to deal with feelings inspired by toxic stress. When faced with patients suffering from these very same symptoms doctors have responded in exactly the same way: by prescribing drugs.

For many years now doctors have attempted to treat patients suffering from toxic stress with tranquillizers. And their attempts to treat such patients have frequently made things worse rather than better. Tranquillizers solve none of the fears or anxieties caused by toxic stress. Indeed, because they are themselves frequently addictive and because the list of side effects associated with their use seems endless, tranquillizers have created new problems. Time and time again doctors and drug companies have created new forms of addiction by rash prescribing practices, by a willingness to promote and prescribe drugs which have not been thoroughly tested and by an enthusiasm for the new which is rarely tempered by scepticism or suspicion.

There is, sadly, no doubt that one of the major factors in the rising incidence of drug addiction in recent years has been the role played by the medical profession. (And one of the true ironies of health care in the twentieth century is the fact that a huge speciality within the profession has been formed to deal with problems largely created by doctors themselves). A small part of the problem has been caused by the deliberate and callous provision of drugs for money, but the greater part of the problem results from carelessness and simple ignorance.

The precise size of the part played by doctors in our modern drug addiction problem is impossible to estimate. Too many other factors are involved. But the significance of the medical contribution is well illustrated by specific illustrations; by the way that the heroin problem developed in Britain in the 1960s for example. There were, at that time, relatively few heroin addicts in Britain (no more than a few score) and no one took the problem very seriously. Although steps had been taken in other countries to control the supply of heroin through specialist centres, British doctors insisted on retaining their prescribing freedom. It was argued that if doctors simply gave the addicts they saw the precise amount of heroin that they needed, then the problem could be controlled without too much difficulty. The main advantage of this system was seen as the fact that it would keep the black marketeers out of the country. If heroin addicts could get their supplies without any difficulty there would be no incentive for smugglers to move in (in fact the number of addicts was so small that there was no incentive for drug smugglers anyway).

The system broke down because it relied on doctors prescribing the right quantities. The relatively small number of doctors who were prepared to prescribe heroin for addicts wildly overprescribed – sometimes through carelessness, sometimes through gullibility and often through straightforward greed. There were never more than about half a dozen doctors prescribing for Britain's addicts in the 1960s but working mainly in and around fashionable and expensive Harley

Street these doctors helped to create Britain's heroin problem by prescribing in such huge quantities that their patients were able to sell their excess supplies. Within a remarkably short time the number of heroin addicts in London had multiplied many times. And by the time the authorities stepped in the situation was perfect for the smugglers: there were now enough addicts to make an illegal business venture worthwhile.

In just one year in the 1960s 42 kilograms of the 46 kilograms used for medical treatment was prescribed by six doctors. Lady Isabella Frankau, a doctor who practised in Wimpole Street in London, was singlehandedly responsible for the prescribing of hundreds of thousands of heroin tablets to addicts. In 1967 Dr John Petro took over her practice when she died and in a single month he prescribed 24,906 drug ampoules to 110 patients. Well into the 1960s all the drug seizures which were made by the authorities consisted of pure pharmaceutical heroin or cocaine – none of it had been smuggled into the country or 'cut' with a dilutant because there was no market for drug smugglers to exploit.

Tragically, nothing much has changed. Even in the 1980s a doctor said to have written up to 10,000 private prescriptions a year (and to have charged £10 for every prescription) was suspended from practice. It is hardy surprising that in the early 1980s Mr H.B. Spear, Chief Inspector at the Home Office Drugs Branch in London, wrote that 'the overspill from doctors' prescribing has for many years been a major element in the UK illicit market in controlled drugs'.

Apart from these crude examples of greed and gullibility, doctors as a breed are far too easily corrupted, too willing to accept what they are told by drug company representatives and too quick to leap at the chance to prescribe 'new' drugs. Time and time again they have offered their patients untried compounds as a cure or as an alternative for well established ones, and time and time again doctors have created a new and more vicious form of addiction than was known before. Doctors created and promoted morphine as a cure for opium addiction. Doctors created and promoted heroin as a cure for morphine addiction. Doctors created and promoted methadone as a cure for heroin addiction. Doctors told their patients that bromide was a safe non-addictive treatment for anxiety. When that proved to be untrue (and millions of patients had become hooked on bromide) they recommended the barbiturates as safe and non-addictive. When that proved to be untrue (and millions of patients had become hooked on the barbiturates) they recommended the benzodiazepines as safe and non-addictive.

Medical solutions are not the answer

With all these drugs the major factor behind the development of the problem has been that doctors have sought a medical solution to social problems. Traditionally, doctors are trained to think in simple, straightforward terms. They see all disorders starting as a result of biological, chemical or electrical abnormalities and they invariably regard drugs as the primary treatment of choice. Tragically, many of the symptoms that patients take into the doctor's surgery these days are caused by social problems for which there can be no pharmacological answer. And although doctors will tell a drinker that it is dangerous to take alcohol in an attempt to relieve real life problems (for that is how alcoholism often starts), the same doctors will prescribe drugs such as the barbiturates and the benzodiazepines for patients who have physical or mental symptoms caused by social problems for which, similarly, there is not and cannot possibly be any pharmacological solution. If the drug works and suppresses the patient's symptoms, then addiction is almost inevitable, for the patient will learn that as soon as he stops taking the drug that has been prescribed his original, unpleasant symptoms will recur. Any drug that is given to treat anxiety must, if it works, be addictive.

And, of course, whether an individual becomes an addict through his own poor choices, through ill luck or through the errors of a physician, he will still be regarded as an addict. The stigma is the same. Millions of individuals who have become hooked through absolutely no fault of their own are treated badly by doctors, by society and by employers. During the last two decades I have received tens of thousands of letters from people whose lives have been ruined (in every possible sense of the word) because of benzodiazepine addiction. Most report that the agony of their addiction has been compounded by the feelings of shame and guilt they have been encouraged to bear, and by the sense of outrage they feel at the way they have been treated.

Thousands of patients have died because of the arrogance and stupidity of the medical profession. We hear about the deaths of the movie and rock stars such as Jimmi Hendrix, Elvis Presley (when he died Presley was obscenely fat and incoherent and had to wear a nappy because of incontinence caused by his addiction to a wide range of prescribed drugs – one doctor alone admitted prescribing ten thousand pills for the singer in the last twenty months of his life), Janice Joplin, Jim Morrison, Keith Moon, Brian Epstein and John Belushi (most of whom took prescription drugs in addition to illegal substances) but we never hear about the thousands of clerks, mechanics and housewives who die after being given prescribed drugs. Drug companies have repeatedly produced new drugs (and variations on existing products) which are neither necessary nor safe and have then heavily promoted those products to an eager mass market, eventually expressing surprise when their drugs have turned out to be addictive. Drug companies have encouraged expectations about drugs and they have encouraged the acceptability of drug use. Doctors and drug companies have, without a doubt, produced infinitely more addiction and more misery than all the cocaine and heroin pushers of the world combined. In most large cities there are scores of doctors earning huge amounts of money by handing out prescriptions for favourite drugs.

The fact is that drugs – whether prescribed, bought over the counter, bought at an off licence or obtained illegally – are not any sort of answer because neither toxic stress nor the syndrome it produces (which I call 'the twentieth-century blues') are essentially medical problems. The word 'toxic' is a synonym for 'poisonous' and toxic stress is an insidious, morally and spiritually destructive disease. It eats away at the soul but it is not a disease that is ever likely to respond to any pharmacological therapy. The twentieth-century blues is a disorder of the soul rather than the mind; a disease of the spirit rather than the body. Indeed, the additional cruel irony is that by taking a drug a patient will be less and less likely ever to solve his problem. By numbing an individual's mind and slowing down his thought processes (which is what all anti-anxiety drugs do) the doctor damages the patient's ability to deal with his real problems. And so the trap is tightened and complete. The patient's circle of addiction is turned into a restrictive noose from which there is no escape. Most of us will buy a friend a drink if we know he is nervous or anxious. In our hearts we know that it probably is not the sensible thing to do but we do it out of compassion. But that is exactly what has been happening in doctors' surgeries for decades, except that instead of buying their patients a single evening of blissful forgetfulness, doctors are prescribing blissful forgetfulness by the month.

What is perhaps most surprising about the fact that doctors continue to prescribe drugs for the treatment of anxiety is that they persist in the belief that there will one day be a drug available that will work without producing addiction. That suggests an ignorance of the human spirit (and an ignorance about drugs) which should worry us all. For it is not the drug alone that produces the addiction; it is the combination of the drug, the individual's needs and his circumstances. And of those three the nature of the drug is perhaps of least significance. It is impossible to produce any effective relief from anxiety and not run the risk of producing an addiction to the agent responsible for providing the relief.

During the last two decades the demand for drugs has grown so rapidly that doctors have had to introduce more 'efficient' schemes for handing out prescriptions. For example, many now provide tranquillizers and sleeping tablets on repeat prescriptions. This means that patients can get a supply of tablets without going anywhere near the surgery or the doctor. A telephone call or a letter to the receptionist results in a prescription being left out for collection or sent back by return mail. The repeat prescribing of modern drugs is one of the major reasons why there are so many addicts around today.

Most frightening of all is the fact that despite the existence of an enormous amount of evidence to show that new drugs which are described as non-addictive almost invariably turn out to be addictive, many doctors seem consistently enthusiastic about new products, accepting the manufacturers' claims with remarkably little cynicism. The only possible explanation is that doctors are addicted to prescribing just as much as their patients are addicted to swallowing. The reason for this professional addiction is simple: doctors do not know what else to do. Much of the time they spend struggling to deal with problems for which they have never had any formal training. Doctors are trained to deal with physical disorders and physical symptoms but today the high levels of stress that patients are under mean that most of their patients have psychological problems and mental symptoms.

The traditional medical answer to a physical problem is to prescribe a drug – just a hundred years or so ago, doctors did not get paid anything *unless* they handed over a prescription – and so doctors prescribe drugs because they have nothing else to offer.

There are two final reasons why drug addiction is so common – and is, despite the war being fought by politicians and legislators, getting commoner.

The first of these is cost.

It may sound obvious but the price of a drug has a tremendous influence on the number of people taking it. Children sniff glue not because it is better than anything else, or even more available, but because it is one of the cheapest psychoactive drugs available. Despite their avowed determination to reduce drug consumption, governments have rarely used price as a serious restricting factor on the sale of addictive drugs. During recent years in Britain the real cost of alcohol has steadily declined. Today it takes roughly half as long to earn the price of a pint of beer as it did thirty years ago. There seems little doubt that a modest increase in the price of alcohol would result in a fall in the amount of alcohol being consumed. A study done by a team of researchers in Edinburgh, Scotland showed that the single most frequently cited reason for cutting down on alcohol consumption was the price. Even heavy drinkers said that they always cut down when the price went up.

There can be little doubt that governments which are reluctant to raise taxes on abused and addictive products such as alcohol and tobacco are unwilling to risk the loss in revenue that they fear might result and are more concerned about their own short-term finances than about the long-term health of their electorates.

The other major influence on drug use and abuse is fashion. There are individual fashions in drugs just as there are fashions in clothes and motor cars. Cocaine is an upper class drug. Benzodiazepines and barbiturates and amphetamines are middle class drugs. Heroin is a lower class drug. At any one time there will be specific drug fashions in specific areas.

But it is the fact that drugs in general are fashionable that we should worry most about. Children grow up in our society regarding drugs as a normal part of everyday life; they see their parents using drugs to avoid conception, to get to sleep and to treat mild headaches. It is hardly surprising that children grow up to accept that drugs can be used to help eradicate boredom, to help deal with pressure and to cope with a heavy work load. Our familiarity with drugs has led to contempt for the dangers associated with them. We have learned to use drugs and to take advantage of their powers but we have not yet learned to fear them.

Prevention rather than cure

Our attempts to deal with drug addiction have proved fruitless and ineffective and there can be little doubt that the size of the world's drug addiction problem would be much smaller if those responsible for organizing treatment programmes had put more thought into what they do. The most important mistake they have made has been to concentrate their efforts almost entirely on the period during and immediately after withdrawal. They have assumed that these are the difficult moments when addicts need the maximum amount of support. They are, however, wrong.

Ex-addicts need help to re-establish themselves and to survive without drugs long after the days of withdrawal, not because of any direct physiological hangover effect of the drug they have taken but because of the fact that they usually remain in the same social, financial and personal environment where they first got into trouble. If they are to give up their drug they must also abandon their friends and their adopted culture and return to boredom, emptiness and a sense of worthlessness. With temptation and opportunity remaining and with those around them using the drugs they are trying to avoid, it is hardly surprising that so many people succumb shortly after giving up. Those struggling to help 'cure' drug addicts should remember that at least nine out of ten dieters fail – a worse failure rate than that endured by heroin addicts. This is not because food is even more addictive than heroin but because would-be slimmers have to struggle to eat less in a world where advertizing campaigns are constantly being waged in an attempt to get everyone to eat more.

Way back in 1926 the Rolleston Committee (set up to investigate drug addiction) announced that 'relapse, sooner or later, appears to be the rule' and recommended that addicts who failed to break their addiction should simply be maintained on their drug for life. Alarmingly, this defeatist attitude is still popular among some doctors and many politicians who are either unable or unwilling to understand the link between drug addiction and social circumstances. Our treatment of addicts is illogical, poorly thought out and badly sustained. In *The Law and the Treatment of Drug and Alcohol Dependent Persons* (published by the World Health Organization) Porter, Arif and Curran list no fewer than twelve different approaches to detoxification from opiates. Whenever the experts are split and cannot decide which type of treatment works best, it is safest to assume that no form of treatment works well.

Our understanding of addiction as a phenomenon is about as far advanced as our understanding of mental illness was two centuries ago. Most governments around the world put most of their emphasis on the harassment of users as much as suppliers rather than on the provision of any sort of effective, constructive treatment programme or any attempt to prevent the development of addiction. Even those involved in the specific treatment of addiction often seem ignorant of the fact that treatment aimed at an addiction itself is worthless without any attempt to deal with the root causes of addiction. And those who organize treatment programmes seldom seem to understand that the absence of a drug frequently leaves an addict with a void in his life; many addicts are addicted to their addiction, hooked on the paraphernalia of their addiction and obsessed by the constant need to fulfill the needs of their addiction.

Programmes for drug addicts seem based on the simple idea of forcing the addict to stop using the drug he is addicted to. This is as logical as forcing someone suffering from anorexia nervosa to eat. If you force an anorexic to eat, you may manage a short-term solution to the symptoms, but you will not find a solution to the basic cause of the problem.

The incompetence of many of those who are paid to help drug addicts is illustrated more than adequately by the type of campaign routinely organized by such groups. Failing to understand that many young users are frightened neither by the physical dangers nor the legal threats, many posters and television advertizements have been prepared showing emaciated James Dean types standing alone, moody, angry and emaciated. The aim is, presumably, to shock and frighten the would-be addict. But such advertizements are more likely to attract the rebellious youth than to repel him. How can you use normal advertizing techniques to induce a sense of fear in someone who injects heroin directly into his penis or the end of his nose? How can anyone hope to use normal techniques to induce anxiety in someone who injects melted cheese and salad cream into his veins when he cannot get hold of his normal drug?

Danger inspires curiosity among the young who have a poorly developed sense of their own mortality. Motorbikes, unprotected sex and bunjee jumping are all popular with the young because of the danger, not despite it. Addicts are notoriously unreliable and anti-authoritarian; they are unlikely to be put off or convinced by authoritarian advertizements. The risks, the danger and the lawlessness are part of the attraction. As *Rolling Stone* editors Ira Mothner and Alan Weitz point out in their book *How to Get Off Drugs*, many youngsters keep on using drugs not *in spite of* their fears but *because of them*. What we must all remember is that studies performed in the 1960s showed that two out of five smokers were made depressed by their first attempt at smoking cigarettes and most felt sick, but they put up with the unpleasant symptoms and persevered because the peer pressure was greater than the discomfort. Getting high is a puberty rite and youngsters use drugs to boost their self-confidence. Taking drugs helps defy authority, it enables youngsters to show that they are brave and it is something they can do alone. When the police raid drug parties they are encouraging more parties by giving the users of drugs a purpose; drug raids encourage drug use. The demand for mind-altering drugs is age old and irresistible.

It is also worth pointing out here that the tendency in some clinics for those offering help and advice to insist on including a lecture on the hazards of drug use as an essential ingredient of their treatment programme is bound to be counter-productive. If patients visiting sexual disease clinics had to put up with a talk about the perils of promiscuity every time they sought help, there would be a black market in antibiotics.

The hypocrisy of the legislators

The final reason why drug use is going up is undoubtedly the hypocrisy exemplified by the double-edged approach to drug use taken by politicians and legislators. The hypocrisy is usually inspired by commercial interest and enhanced by political expediency but it is always initiated by the arbitrary and illogical ways in which drugs are chosen to be put on the 'forbidden' list. Drugs are not banned because of the damage that they do to the individual; they are not banned to discourage their use by others; they are not banned because of the damage users do to other members of society and they are not banned because of the cost to society. If drugs were banned for any of these reasons then tobacco and alcohol would be banned and heroin, cocaine and cannabis might be freely available.

Consider, for example, the way that cannabis got itself listed as a dangerous drug alongside the far more dangerous opiates. It is, indeed, difficult to find a drug which better illustrates the illogicality and pointlessness of drug control legislation or which illustrates more dramatically the hypocrisy of those who are entrenched opponents of drug use.

Back in the nineteenth century cannabis was used in Britain to help opium eaters kick their habit (history is full of these absurdities) and the drug is so mild in its effects that the chances are that it would have remained a fairly obscure drug

The Drugs Myth

had not a Dr Warnock, then Superintendent of the Cairo Asylum in Egypt, written a report suggesting that cannabis might be the cause of insanity. Dr Warnock wrote his report in 1895 and it seems likely that he came to his conclusion because many of the inmates in the asylum where he worked were enthusiastic cannabis users. What Dr Warnock seems to have overlooked is the fact that cannabis was extremely popular outside the asylum too.

Dr Warnock was very much out on his own when he wrote his report. Other experts who had studied cannabis had all come to a very different conclusion. For example, the Indian Hemp Drugs Commission of 1893-4 was set up to examine the trade in hemp drugs such as cannabis and their effect on the social and moral condition of the people of India. The Commission had been given the job of deciding whether or not cannabis should be made illegal and its conclusion was that the physical, mental and moral effects of cannabis were not adverse and that there was no evidence of cannabis leading to addiction. All the available evidence suggested that cannabis was no more damaging a drug than tea or coffee.

But Dr Warnock's isolated and rather eccentric and poorly based opinion became of vital importance in 1925 when Britain, together with a number of other countries, signed the International Opium Convention. The Convention was designed to introduce binding international controls on the sale of opium and cannabis was included along with the far more dangerous opiates as a result of pressure from Egypt where people still believed Dr Warnock's solitary report and assumed that the regular use of cannabis could lead to mental illness. Britain and the other signatories accepted Egypt's bizarre request to include cannabis on the list of controlled drugs since it seemed, at the time, to be a fairly modest and almost irrelevant concession. The outlawing of cannabis, one of the world's most harmless drugs, was regarded as a small price to pay for persuading Egypt to sign the international opium ban. Ever since 1925 cannabis has remained on the 'controlled' drug list and, despite the continued absence of any evidence to show that it is a dangerous drug, politicians have steadfastly refused to reconsider its status. And yet cannabis is no more dangerous than caffeine or chocolate, and if Dr Warnock had written his paper about those substances the chances are that they would today be regarded as dangerous drugs and would be sold on street corners in small packages for high prices, while cannabis would be sold in corner shops and advertized freely on television to children.

Compare the way politicians and legislators treat cannabis to the way the same people treat alcohol and tobacco and the contrast is startling.

Some politicians claim that tobacco and alcohol get special treatment because they bring in huge amounts of revenue which are needed to lubricate social services. This is, quite simply, untrue.

Tobacco and alcohol don't simply cost society an enormous amount in damaged lives but they also cost society a vast fortune in cash, for the cost to society of all the damage done by these two drugs far exceeds the revenue. In a paper entitled 'The Taxes of Sin: Do Smokers and Drinkers Pay Their Way?' a team of specialists writing in the *Journal of the American Medical Association* in 1989 concluded that 'poor health habits, such as smoking and heavy drinking, carry costs not only for smokers and heavy drinkers, but for everyone else as well'. After a careful study of collectively financed health insurance, pensions, disability insurance, group life insurance, fires, motor vehicle accidents and the criminal justice system, they concluded that 'nonsmokers subsidize smokers' medical care and group life insurance' and that 'excise taxes on alcohol cover only about half the costs imposed on others'. Estimates in the UK support the conclusion that the taxes paid by smokers and drinkers are insufficient to pay for the social costs of their habits.

4 | Heroin, cocaine, cannabis and LSD

Heroin, cocaine and cannabis – why these drugs are not as dangerous as some people would have us believe.

When journalists write about 'drugs' and politicians talk about them they are usually referring to three particular drugs: heroin, cocaine and cannabis. The implication is always that these three drugs are particularly dangerous and exceptionally addictive and it is upon this theory that some of the legislation and most of the law enforcement agencies designed to control the sale and use of these drugs are founded. The principle of the entire illegal drug philosophy would be considerably weakened if it could be shown that these three drugs are no more dangerous or addictive than many other legally available drugs.

In this chapter I intend to show not only how these drugs came to achieve widespread popularity and how, in many cases, laws have had exactly the opposite effect on drug taking to the one intended, but also why I believe that these three drugs are not only no more dangerous or addictive than other drugs but are *less* dangerous and *less* addictive than tobacco, alcohol and the benzodiazepines. In the next chapter I will describe some of the drugs which I and other drug experts believe to be more dangerous and more addictive than heroin, cocaine or cannabis – and to cause far more physical and mental distress.

This argument is vitally important, for once it becomes clear that the legislation governing drug use is designed to control three of the least dangerous psychoactive drugs (the legislation was, after all, developed over half a century ago when our knowledge about these drugs was primitive to say the least) the only logical steps are either to decriminalize heroin, cocaine and cannabis or to outlaw alcohol, tobacco and the benzodiazepines. Since the second of these choices would be unworkable (for the same reason that the attempts to control the use of drugs currently made illegal has failed) the only sensible plan is decriminalization.

The opiates: heroin, morphine and opium

Heroin, morphine and opium are all narcotic drugs which are derived from the same basic source and produce similar effects on people who take them. Extracted from the oriental poppy plant which grows – very easily and in poor soil – in such varied places as India, Turkey, China, Russia, Egypt and Mexico, these narcotics all depress the central nervous system, relieve pain, induce sleep, cure coughing and diarrhoea and can produce an extraordinary feeling of comfort and well-being. They make stress and worry fade away and create a pleasant, euphoric feeling. Like all psychoactive drugs, opium and its derivatives have a pleasant and mood-altering effect. That is, after all, why people use them. Not many people get hooked on drugs which invariably make you sick and which make your hair fall out.

The basic product obtained from the poppy plant – opium – is the dried juice from the plant's pods. When pods are cut open white juice oozes out and quickly turns a deep reddish brown as it oxidizes in the air, eventually hardening into balls of gum which have a sweet smell and a bitter taste.

Opium has been used for thousands of years. The ancient Greeks and Romans called it 'the destroyer of grief', while the ancient Egyptians used it for a variety of purposes – including quietening crying children. We tend to associate the opium poppy with the Far East but it was not until Arab traders carried it there in the sixteenth century that the drug became popular in either China or India.

By the seventeenth century opium had reached most of Europe and Thomas Sydenham, one of the great fathers of English medicine and a renowned teacher and physician, recommended it for the treatment of pain and for helping patients to rest and to sleep. British doctors did not have many drugs available at the time and took to opium with tremendous enthusiasm. Within a century or so it was being wildly overused in England and one worried observer pointed out that its use to deal with hysterics and nervous disorders was like giving pills to try and 'purge folly'. Opium was to eighteenth-century England what the bromides, barbiturates and benzodiazepines have been to the world in the twentieth century.

But it was in China that the opium drug caught on in a really big way. The poppy plants grew easily in India and so there was no shortage for British companies to export to the Chinese mainland. By the nineteenth century the Chinese rulers had recognized the damage that the drug was doing and twice went to war with the British, whose trade domination of the Chinese mainland was dependent on opium. The British won both wars and in the mid-nineteenth century the opium trade became legal. Those British victories – just a century or so ago – led to major problems around the world. It was the legalization of opium in the Far East that led to its widespread use in the United States a few years later.

For most of the nineteenth century opium was available at modest prices just about anywhere in the world; it could be bought in local stores or by mail order and it was sold for a thousand and one different purposes. In most countries it was sold without any restrictions and was generally regarded as a useful home medicine. People used it to help them sober up when they had been drinking too much (in the history of drug use it is clear that time and time again drugs gain popularity when first used to deal with the after effects, side effects or withdrawal effects of other drugs) and parents used to treat their children with it when they developed gastro-intestinal infections and diarrhoea from drinking foul, infected water. Poor water supplies, inadequate sewage facilities and terrible overcrowding in the cities caused thousands to suffer from disorders such as cholera. Doctors could not cure the medical problems, but opium did ease the pains, control the diarrhoea and help people forget their misery.

When the widespread use of opium led to numerous cases of opium overdosage (and many deaths) the authorities in England introduced the 1868 Pharmacy Act to control the sale and availability of opium. However, at that time physicians and apothecaries were fighting for power within the medical profession and so the 1868 Act was kept weak. In practice all the new legislation meant was that if you wanted to buy opium you had to buy it from someone with an officially accepted qualification. This new law did not affect the number of people using opium at all; it just meant that the profits relating to its sale were channelled into the hands of the medical and pharmaceutical professions. To put it bluntly opium was still easily available but it had to be bought from a registered pharmacist. The 1868 Act was a cynical piece of commercial exploitation which was weakened even further by the fact that pressure from patent medicine manufacturers ensured that patent medicines containing opium were excluded from the Act. (As a result of this amendment to the 1868 legislation some products containing opium were still available in Britain over the counter – without a prescription – as recently as the 1970s).

The popularity of opium and the rapidly developing newly born pharmaceutical industry meant that pharmacists were bound to begin experimenting with 'improvements' on the original drug and that is exactly what happened. Morphine was the first new drug to be obtained from opium; it is a chemically refined version of opium and has very similar qualities but is ten times as powerful as raw opium. When morphine was first introduced it was recommended and widely prescribed as an entirely safe, non-addictive alternative to opium – recommended, ironically, as particularly suitable for people who seemed to be hooked on opium. Heroin, which is twenty to twenty-five times as powerful as morphine and twice as addictive came next, and was again promoted as a safe, non-addictive alternative to opium (and as a useful aid for patients hooked on morphine).

Heroin has the classic bitter taste of opium but does not have any smell. In its pure state it is a greyish brown in colour but when diluted it becomes white. The main problem with heroin is that the human body becomes very tolerant to it within a relatively short time and to get the same effect it is necessary to take increasingly massive doses. However, another development had enabled heroin users to overcome this problem. On 28 November 1853 the first hypodermic injection was given to an elderly spinster in Edinburgh by a man called Alexander Wood who used sherry as a solvent for the morphine on the grounds that it would be less likely than water to rust the syringe. Doctors quickly became enthusiastic about this new method of using an opium product and many claimed that it was safer and less likely to lead to problems than the old-fashioned ways of using drugs of this type. The result was that doctors managed to combine a new and more powerful version of opium with a new and more powerful way of giving it and during the later part of the nineteenth century and the first part of the twentieth century more and more people started to use opium extracts – often without any realization that the amount of drug being used could have a particularly dangerous effect.

Eventually, the politicians and lawyers and doctors in Britain began to realize that the widespread use of opium-related products was beginning to create more and more problems, so a series of laws were introduced in an attempt to control their use. However, it was not legislation but social improvements which led to a reduction in the demand for the opiates. By the time the Dangerous Drugs Act was introduced in 1920, the number of people using opium, morphine and heroin regularly had fallen dramatically, largely because under the leadership of social reformers such as Edwin Chadwick, Britain had built an impressive series of sewage works, water supplies and other public services which had dramatically reduced the incidence of cholera and other gastro-intestinal problems and had therefore reduced the need for the diarrhoea-stopping qualities of the opiates.

Around the rest of the world, however, social problems were still commonplace and the continuing and widespread use of the opiates meant that more and more countries were making attempts to control the use of these drugs not by providing better social facilities but by introducing new laws. Laws are, after all, far cheaper than water purification plants, sewage disposal plants and better housing.

By the middle of the twentieth century it was almost universally agreed that the only real answer was to make heroin (the most concentrated and therefore the most dangerous form of opium) totally illegal. It was argued that making the drug completely illegal would make it much easier for the police to extinguish the drug's use.

There were two snags to this theory.

First, this international attempt to outlaw heroin was left with a single legal loophole. Inspired perhaps by the Far Eastern traders who had encouraged the country to fight a war with China to protect the sale of opium, Britain's doctors argued that heroin's powerful pain relieving qualities made it an essential drug and insisted that they would not allow it to be outlawed.

Second, as soon as the drug became illegal in most parts of the world the international crime industry, which had recently been thwarted by the ending of prohibition in America and left with a massive network of sales outlets and tough employees with nothing much to do, enthusiastically took over the supply of the drug. To increase their profits they began the enormously harmful habit of diluting the heroin they sold and it is this more than anything else which has made illegally obtained heroin dangerous. Users face two hazards: first, they do not know for certain how strong the heroin is that they are using and so it is easy to accidentally take an overdose; second, the chemicals used to dilute the heroin include talcum powder, baking soda, brick dust and other far more poisonous substances.

Because Britain's doctors had retained the right to continue prescribing heroin, Britain remained virtually immune to the gangsters selling the drug. It was not worth their while taking the inevitable risks associated with importing heroin into Britain when British users could still obtain the drug on prescription.

If all British doctors had been sensible and honest, Britain might well have remained aloof from the rapidly growing illegal market. However, the small number of London doctors who were prescribing heroin were so pen happy that Britain's small number of heroin addicts soon found themselves up to their knees in heroin prescriptions and to make extra cash they enthusiastically sold on their unwanted supplies to friends who were not addicts but were willing to try the drug. On one occasion one doctor in Harley Street prescribed 900 heroin tablets for a single addict and then, three days later, prescribed another 600 tablets for the same addict. It was not unknown for doctors to sign prescriptions for over 1,000 heroin tablets at a time. The doctors could not be prosecuted because they were acting within the law and their professional freedom to prescribe could not be questioned.

The British medical establishment had created a perfect situation for an illegal drug market. The heroin addicts who had excess supplies sold off what they did not need and in order to create a profitable market for themselves encouraged their friends and neighbours to start using the drug. Those few British doctors spawned the first of the country's drug pushers. After all, one of the classic ways of acquiring a drug market is to give away free supplies of a drug to non-users who try the free sample, like it and then have to pay for their supplies. This technique is regularly used by professional drug pushers. Incidentally, shortly after the benzodiazepines were first introduced into Britain supplies were donated free to hospitals in order to calm government anxieties about the cost. This mass marketing programme must surely have helped lead to the massive addiction problem which now exists.

By the time British politicians realized that they had made a mistake in allowing doctors to retain their prescribing freedom, it was too late. In 1968 new regulations were introduced, ensuring that doctors had to be licensed and drug addicts had to be notified to the Home Office. This meant that the addicts who had been created by the prescribing bonanza of the 1960s were now in difficulty and could no longer obtain their supplies quite so easily – and they certainly could no longer make a profit by selling supplies they did not need. The scene was set for smugglers and drug dealers to enter the British market and to start selling heroin. The increased number of addicts and the shortage of heroin made the situation perfect for the illegal suppliers. If the British had sat down and worked out a way to create an illegal drug culture in Britain, they could not have done it more efficiently or more effectively.

As the demand in Britain has grown so the drug pushers have grown too and the number of addicts has started to explode for two reasons: first, those selling drugs do not have to rely on subtle marketing techniques, they can terrorize their customers into buying; second, those who are already hooked usually have to turn to crime to raise cash to pay for their habits. Some try thieving or prostitution. But most discover that the easiest way to raise money is to start dealing and pushing the drug to which they themselves are addicted. And since pushers who try selling to other people's addicts don't stay alive long, that means creating new addicts.

The history of the opiates shows that the long-term physical effects are remarkably light. The long-term heroin user will be physically weak and debilitated; he will have lost weight and may have infections – particularly at injection sites – and he will probably be constipated. But there is unlikely to be any significant physical or mental damage. The opiates are physically fairly benign and cause very little organic damage; they do not cause cancer or heart disease and they do not destroy the brain or the liver. Heroin decreases violent tendencies and sexual appetite and does not lead to the sort of impaired judgement and lowered self-control associated with alcohol.

The dangers associated with its use arise for two reasons. First, users run a real risk of overdosing or poisoning themselves because there is never any way for them to tell just how pure a batch of heroin may be – nor of telling what impurities it may contain. Also the use of infected or dirty needles dramatically increases their chances of suffering from AIDS, hepatitis and other potentially lethal infections. Second, because the illegally supplied drug is extremely expensive, addicts tend to neglect themselves and dedicate themselves almost exclusively to the search for fresh supplies or for the money to pay for fresh supplies. They run the risk of getting into trouble with the law and since they usually buy from people who use violence as a business tool they run the risk of being killed by their suppliers. The physical and mental hazards associated with the use of heroin, morphine and the other opiates are largely a result of the fact that the drugs are illegal. It is their very illegality which makes them dangerous rather than any inherent physical danger derived from their pharmacological properties. Both alcohol and tobacco cause considerably more damage to the human body than any of the opiates. Even caffeine – the most easily available drug there is – causes more physical upheaval than heroin.

As to the addictive quality of these drugs, that has undoubtedly been wildly exaggerated by those who want to glamorize the drugs (in films and books), by addicts who want an excuse to continue using their favourite drug and by the police and the legislators who want support for their opposition to the drugs. The truth is, however, that although coming off heroin can be hazardous and extremely unpleasant, the symptoms associated with withdrawal are usually described in textbooks as being the symptoms of influenza – chills, nausea, vomiting, sweating and muscular pains – and are likely to last no longer than a bout of influenza. Withdrawal usually lasts around five days and is extremely unlikely to last more than two weeks at most. Giving up heroin 'cold turkey' (in other words stopping it suddenly) leads to a cold feeling on the skin and raised goose pimples (that is why it is called cold turkey) and is nowhere near as dramatic as some recent films have suggested. According to a report published in the journal *Medical News* in 1984, heroin addicts should be able to deal with the symptoms of withdrawal by using mild pain-killers, relaxation exercises, hot water bottles and plenty of warm baths. Despite its reputation heroin is not particularly addictive and around ninety per cent of the people who try it for a few times give it up without any real difficulty. The amphetamines, barbiturates and benzodiazepines are all considerably more addictive than any of the opiates.

The tragedy as far as heroin withdrawal is concerned is that doctors have repeatedly introduced withdrawal 'treatments' for heroin which have in practice simply replaced one set of problems with another. The theory behind replacement therapy is that it is possible to ease an addict through the pangs of withdrawal and minimize the unpleasant effects, but in practice the substances used usually cause as many problems as the drug which is the subject of withdrawal. The one product most commonly associated with heroin withdrawal is methadone, first introduced as a withdrawal treatment in America in the early 1960s. At that time it was claimed that methadone was safe and that the side effects associated with it were mild. Sadly, within less than a decade it had become clear that by using methadone doctors were merely exchanging one form of addiction for another. Less than a decade after methadone was introduced there were 80,000 methadone addicts in the United States of America and today methadone addiction is a recognised major international drug problem. There is now a black market in methadone.

▬▬▬ Cocaine

Although it is not usually regarded as being as dangerous or as addictive as heroin, there is little doubt that cocaine is rapidly becoming another *bête blanche* as far as politicians and legislators are concerned. During the last few years an astonishing amount of disinformation about cocaine and derivatives such as 'crack' has been written and broadcast. It is difficult to avoid the conclusion that the bad reputation cocaine is gaining fits the purposes of the legislators very well. The more fearsome a reputation cocaine has, the easier it is to support the laws which outlaw its use.

The truth is that although cocaine is probably more physically hazardous than heroin, and is almost certainly just as addictive, it is neither as physically dangerous as tobacco or alcohol nor as addictive as the benzodiazepines.

Cocaine is a modern, scientific derivative of coca leaves and for the natives of Bolivia, Peru and Argentina and the hillsides of the Andes, coca leaf chewing is a peaceful, harmless way of dealing with stress, pressure and a cruel environment. The natives of these countries started chewing coca leaves and making tea from them hundreds of years ago and never really ran into any trouble.

To begin with, the habit was confined to a fairly select few within the Inca empire; religious leaders and civic authorities being among the relatively small number of people allowed access to the leaves. But even when the Spanish conquerors of

The Drugs Myth

South America discovered the benefits of the leaves and encouraged the locals to use them more widely, there were still no really unpleasant or unpredictable consequences. The Spanish used the leaves as a form of local currency – paying mine workers with small bundles of coca leaves – and took full advantage of the fact that chewing the leaves produces a sense of well-being that helps the user forget discomfort, stress and pain.

The Spanish connection inevitably meant that coca leaves were introduced into Europe in the nineteenth century but they never really caught on, although some doctors did recommend them as a tonic. A Corsican called Angelo Mariani made a small fortune by blending coca leaves with wine and producing a fairly potent mixture which he called Vin Mariani and sold to two popes, four kings and such lions of the French literary establishment as Jules Verne, Alexander Dumas and Emile Zola. But it was only when cocaine was first extracted from the leaves, about 1860, that the coca habit became popular in sophisticated European society. Scientists had, once again, managed to turn a fairly innocuous habit into a far more dangerous addiction.

The new drug, cocaine, had many enthusiastic supporters. English medical journals in the mid 1880s were full of enthusiastic stories of the ways in which cocaine could be used. Many of the papers on the subject appeared in the *British Medical Journal* and cocaine was advocated as a treatment for disorders as varied as cancer, hay fever, sea sickness and nymphomania. It was also fairly widely used as an anaesthetic. The new drug was recommended in *The Lancet* and appeared in a number of widely available patent medicines. In Austria, Sigmund Freud, the psychoanalyst, was an enthusiastic user of cocaine. Apart from using it himself he used it to help morphine addicts and also recommended it for the treatment of tiredness and nervousness. However, although cocaine was often written about and was fashionable it was never widely used. Despite its availability in patent medicines it was expensive to buy in any quantity or strength.

At the start of the twentieth century cocaine started to fall out of favour and by the 1960s its use had fallen dramatically. The only regular users were the Bolivian and Peruvian peasants who were still enthusiastically chewing their unrefined and relatively harmless coca leaves. Coca leaves were still used as payment for labour to workers in distant areas of Peru and Bolivia and coca leaves were widely used socially. It was the custom to pass leaves around at small gatherings and coca leaves were placed on the table for patrons of small bars and clubs in hillside towns and villages. In the Andes, coca leaf chewing was a socially acceptable habit which played the same sort of role as alcohol does in most of the western so-called civilized world. The coca leaf was even used as a medicine in the hill towns – with a hot water infusion or coca leaf tea being used for a wide range of physical and mental problems. As recently as 1980 the World Health Organization reported that there were four million regular coca leaf chewers in South America, with about half the adult population of the central Andes being regular users. Under these circumstances coca leaf causes hardly any problems at all. The usual response to the leaves is a feeling of well-being, quiet and calm. Socially disruptive behaviour after chewing coca leaves is almost unknown and there do not seem to be any hazards or noticeable side effects.

Unfortunately for the natives of South America, the western passion for cocaine returned to the United States in the late 1960s, and it returned with a vengeance even though the drug was illegal. It is difficult to say why it returned to popularity after such a long pause but the fact that the drug was widely used by doctors and dentists as a local anaesthetic had ensured that there always remained a small, hard core of users. The South American hill farmers found that they could increase their income enormously if, instead of selling their coca leaves to other villagers, they used the leaves to produce illegal coca sulfate paste and then exported the paste to North America. The local farmers then found themselves with two problems.

First, they found themselves being harassed by the authorities. US drug control agents traced the supply of cocaine to the Andes and official pressure from the United States ensured that a long-accepted local custom – the growing of coca leaves – became an illegal activity.

Second, the huge profits to be made out of selling cocaine meant that there was now a shortage of coca leaves to sell locally.

The Drugs Myth

Deprived of their coca leaves some of the farmers and peasants had to seek solace in other, far more dangerous drugs.

A third problem developed as a direct result of what was happening in the US. The leaves grown by the South American farmers were converted into cocaine by a huge number of illegal, underground laboratories which had sprung up all over Bolivia, but eventually the amount of cocaine being produced exceeded the demand and there was a glut. The obvious place for the dealers to sell this excess was on the home market where the locals were no longer able to obtain their coca leaves. And so, during the 1970s, a major drug problem was born in the countries of the Andes. The locals took to cocaine quite quickly; those who thought of themselves as cosmopolitan soon regarding coca leaf chewing as a rather primitive, out-of-date habit.

Today, the production of cocaine is big business. Two hundred thousand acres of Peru and Bolivia are devoted to growing coca leaves and most of the crop goes to Colombia to be refined. Very little money is made by the farmers of Bolivia and Peru – the major profits to go the men who turn the leaves into cocaine and then smuggle the drug into North America.

Although coca leaves are virtually harmless, cocaine is far more powerful. The cocaine content of the dry coca leaves is one per cent of their weight whereas the concentration in coca paste (a substance produced during refining) may reach forty-five per cent. An additional problem is produced by the fact that whereas coca leaves are entirely natural, cocaine invariably contains toxic substances and using toxin-rich cocaine can occasionally produce hallucinations, confusion, weight loss, insomnia, anxiety, tremor and irritation. When snorted or sniffed regularly for long periods, cocaine may damage the lining of the nasal passage and the drug can also speed up the heart, and produce a strange, crawly feeling in the skin known as formication. The physical effects are, however, modest compared to those associated with tobacco.

The traditional way for users to take cocaine is either by injection or by sniffing through a straw or a crisp, rolled-up twenty dollar bill, or from a small spoon. To get the best from sniffing the user lays a razor-thin line of cocaine across a piece of smooth glass or metal, closes one nostril and sniffs the line of cocaine through the clear nostril. Cocaine is soluble in water so that when it touches the moist membrane in the nose it dissolves and goes straight into the blood stream. It takes about five minutes to get a kick from inhaling cocaine and the effect can last up to an hour.

There are, however, a number of ways of making cocaine even more dramatic. Although cocaine is itself a refined component of the coca leaf, it is possible to carry the refining process one step further and to free the active drug from its base. This technique is known as 'freebasing' and since the late 1970s shops in America have sold cheap extraction kits designed to enable cocaine users to refine their own cocaine. The highly publicized substance 'crack' is merely a form of refined cocaine. The advantage of refined cocaine or crack is that when heated it vaporizes and it can, therefore, be smoked in the same way as tobacco. The lungs are extremely efficient at absorbing the vapour and when used this way cocaine has a very speedy effect.

Politicians and policemen have often described 'crack' and freebased cocaine as 'instantly addictive' and 'lethally dangerous' but this sort of hype is nonsensical and is inspired largely, I suspect, by a desire for publicity rather than anything else. Politicians live on publicity in the same way that the rest of us live on oxygen and the police have learned that by exaggerating the threats of drugs to society they can obtain more financial resources and more power on the streets. However, the *British Medical Journal* reported in 1989 that a survey of 308 adolescents in Miami showed that nine out of ten had used crack at least once in the previous three months but that only a third were using it daily, with another third using it no more than once or twice a week. Those figures show quite clearly that even crack has low-level addictive qualities. As with heroin it is the impurities and overdoses which seem to lead to the more serious and long-lasting physical problems.

Cannabis

Cannabis is the third illegal drug which attracts an enormous amount of attention from politicians and police officers, and it is the most widely used illicit drug in the world. But despite massive amounts of officially funded research there is still no real evidence to suggest that cannabis is dangerous. A small group of psychiatrists claim that long-term users may suffer from confusion and instability and social alienation, but since most psychiatrists are white and middle class and most cannabis users are black and certainly not middle class, it is probably fair to say that these conclusions are of dubious value. The fact is that there are probably more myths and misunderstandings (many of them inspired by wishful thinking) about cannabis than about any other drug.

Two thousand years ago cannabis was known as 'sacred grass' and in the sixteenth century Indian doctors used it to treat leprosy. In 1893 the Indian Hemp Drugs Commission questioned witnesses who claimed to have seen violent crimes committed by people using hashish but not one of their witnesses could remember any precise details. The Commission – which had been set up to examine the trade in hemp drugs, their effect on the social and moral condition of the people of India and the desirability of prohibiting their cultivation and use – concluded that the physical, mental and moral effects of hemp drugs used in moderation were not adverse, that there was no evidence of cannabis use leading to addiction and that prohibition would be unworkable. Since then a number of surveys and research groups have confirmed that there are no obvious dangers with cannabis, and doctors are now using it in the treatment of the eye disease glaucoma, to help treat the nausea that is associated with the use of chemotherapy for cancer, and to help AIDS patients gain weight. In a paper published in the US *Journal of Clinical Oncology* in July 1991, around five hundred cancer specialists confirmed that they would prescribe smokable marijuana to their patients if it were legal. Indeed over four hundred of the doctors admitted that they had already recommended smoking marijuana to their patients, despite the risk of prosecution.

It seems likely that if there were any real hazards associated with the use of cannabis, they would be fairly well known by now, but all the available evidence suggests that cannabis is no more damaging a drug than tea or coffee. Indeed, it is probably *less* dangerous than drinks containing caffeine. Over fifty million Americans are said to have tried cannabis and around twenty million are said to use it regularly. Nearly half of senior school pupils use it and one survey in 1979 showed that seven per cent of senior school pupils in America used it daily.

Cannabis was introduced into Paris by French intellectuals Baudelaire and Gautier in the middle part of the nineteenth century and thereafter spread throughout Europe. Dr Gabriel Nahas, a United Nations consultant, concluded after a fifteen year study that five million people use the drug in Britain, and in 1984 a spokesman for the British Police Federation admitted that the police did not have the resources to control the possession of cannabis and that the law on possession was 'unenforceable'. Nevertheless far more people are convicted for cannabis offences in Britain than for any other drug – around 25,000 a year.

Cannabis, which grows as easily as a weed and is cheap and easy to collect, is America's second largest cash crop – plantations have now been found in all 155 of America's national parks and the annual income from cannabis cultivation in some national forests is estimated to exceed the revenue for timber. In Jamaica cannabis is a billion pound a year business – and the island's most important crop.

It is inconceivable that a drug could be so widely used without hazards and side effects being noticed by now – particularly since there are so many people constantly looking for evidence to show that the drug is dangerous. Researchers who have spent much time and money investigating cannabis and looking for problems associated with it have managed to find relatively few drawbacks to its use and no serious side effects or associated problems. Cannabis heightens sensations such as touch, sound and smell and makes those who use it feel relaxed and comfortable. But there is no evidence to suggest that it is in any sense of the word a 'dangerous' drug. Those who steadfastly insist on opposing its use are probably more opposed to what they see as the anarchic behaviour of those who use it than to the drug itself.

Technically, cannabis is a sedative and hypnotic. It is produced from the *Cannabis sativa* plant which grows easily and readily all over the world. The active ingredient is tetrahydrocannabinol, produced by the flowering tops and the leaves of the plant and most highly concentrated in the plant's resin. Marijuana is a mixture of the chopped leaves, stems and flowers of the cannabis plant that is prepared for smoking; charas or ganja is the unadulterated resin from the plant and is much stronger than marijuana. Hashish, also stronger than marijuana, is a powdered form of charas.

Ever since Dr Warnock's bizarre and unsustained claims were accepted in order to placate the Egyptians, cannabis has remained on the controlled drug list and legislators, customs and police around the world have continued to harass cannabis users and smugglers. This two-thirds of a century old piece of political bargaining has had important repercussions around the rest of the world.

In Nepal thousands of villagers have had their cannabis crops banned because of local laws introduced to conform with the international ruling. This has caused enormous problems in India where cannabis is used in Hindu religious rites and is regarded as a 'holy' drug, whereas alcohol (a drug which is frequently imported by the same westerners who have sought to see cannabis crops destroyed) is considered dangerous and unacceptable.

There have been similar problems in Jamaica where cannabis has been used without any noticeable ill effects for over a century as a tonic, as a cure for everything from period pains to colds and from impotence to nerve troubles, and as a magic substance to ward off evil spirits. The traditional use among agricultural workers is so widespread that it is not unknown for ganja tea to be put into a baby's feeding bottle and cannabis is frequently cooked and served up with vegetables. The heaviest users of cannabis in Jamaica are probably the Rastafarians who believe that the substance gives them divine powers. The Rastafarians are a black, messianic sect who wear long hair and beards. They worship the late Haile Selassie, emperor of Ethiopia until 1974, and seek repatriation to Ethiopia as a fundamental goal. There are now many thousands of Rastafarians in Jamaica and Britain and for them the legislation controlling cannabis is deeply unjust and about as outrageous as laws controlling communion wine might be to Christians.

Cannabis is usually linked with heroin and cocaine and policemen often argue that one of the main dangers of cannabis is that people who use it are likely to end up using heroin. This is given as one of the main reasons for persecuting and prosecuting people who use cannabis. There are, however, a number of dangers in this argument.

First, as I have already shown, heroin itself is nowhere near as dangerous as some politicians and policemen seem to believe.

Second, since anyone who uses cannabis quickly becomes aware that the drug is not particularly powerful, the law governing other drugs is dramatically weakened by the association. Drug users inevitably assume that since the risks associated with cannabis have been dramatically over-emphasized, then the risks associated with heroin and cocaine have probably been wildly over-emphasized too.

Third, by forcing cannabis users underground and into contact with the black market, the law has given drug pushers a large, affluent market to blackmail and to threaten. Many of the problems which affect cannabis users arise from the fact that the drug they use has to be obtained illegally and puts them into contact with many aspects of crime and violence.

Fourth, most heroin users have previously used tobacco and alcohol. The association between drugs is, therefore, a dangerous argument.

In recent years many attempts have been made to legalize cannabis, but the politicians have invariably backed away from what they have clearly seen as a dangerous move. In 1968 a British committee chaired by Baroness Wootton recommended that the penalties for smoking cannabis be reduced since there was no evidence that it led to violent crime. But Home Secretary James Callaghan refused on the grounds that it would lead people to think that the government was not treating drug taking seriously. In the summer of 1991 a committee of the law reform group Justice (consisting of psychiatrists, lawyers and policemen) recommended that cannabis should be reclassified in a lower category of controlled drugs, with reduced penalties for its possession, production and supply.

LSD and other hallucinogens

LSD (the initials stand for d lysergic acid diethylamide 25) is undoubtedly the best known hallucinogenic drug, but there are many others, some of which occur quite naturally (unlike LSD which is made synthetically in the laboratory). Mescaline, for example, is obtained from a spineless cactus plant native to the south-western United States and Mexico. Psilocybin, another variety of natural hallucinogenic, which is said to have powerful aphrodisiac qualities, is obtained from a type of mushroom which grows quite easily in many parts of the world.

Oddly enough, although the synthetic hallucinogens are carefully controlled drugs, the authorities find it difficult to tell mushrooms where they can or cannot grow and so natural hallucinogens (which can be just as powerful and just as lethal) are, in many countries, far less strictly controlled. In Britain, for example, the law reaches absurd heights when it tries to control magic mushrooms. Some are not controlled at all and some are controlled only when they are deliberately grown and prepared for human consumption, though those who attempt to uphold the law may sometimes find it difficult to define words like 'deliberately' and 'prepared'.

LSD and the other hallucinogens were very popular in the 1960s and 1970s but there always was, and still is, a good deal of confusion about just how they work and what they do. Visual and auditory hallucinations are common, inhibitions disappear and repressed feelings are released. Most users report that the hallucinogens affect their senses in an often quite dramatic way. For example, a piece of fabric or a painting can appear dazzlingly bright and the ticking of a clock can become unbearably loud.

The main danger with the hallucinogens is not that they are addictive (they aren't) but that they can produce serious mental problems – particularly if taken by the wrong individual, in the wrong company at the wrong time. Just who is the right individual to use a hallucinogen and what is the right time to take one is uncertain, although in 1984 a judge sitting in the Inner London Crown Court defended the use of the drug LSD so long as it was taken by 'happy, well-adjusted undergraduates sitting round a fire listening to nice music'.

By labelling cannabis, heroin, cocaine and the hallucinogens as illegal the law makers and law enforcers have created a false sense of security among those who use drugs such as tobacco and alcohol. Those who use 'legal' drugs commonly assume that it is the more dangerous drugs that are 'illegal', and that by choosing the use legally available drugs they are protecting themselves from real hazards. This misconception is dangerous and leads to an enormous amount of illness and many thousands of premature deaths, for the legal and supposedly safe drugs are in practice considerably more dangerous than any of the illegal and supposedly dangerous drugs. I will show in the next chapter just how dangerous this misconception is.

5 | Legal drugs and their dangers

Legal drugs – such as tobacco, alcohol and the benzodiazepines – are more dangerous than illegal ones.

▬▬▬ Alcohol

Although it is regarded with fear, suspicion and loathing in many Far and Middle Eastern countries, alcohol plays a vital role in most western societies. It is difficult to imagine a film, a popular play or a television soap opera in which there is no pub or bar in which the characters can spend a good deal of their time serving or drinking beer or spirits; the governments of most western countries rely heavily on the money they raise by taxing alcohol; many western religions use alcohol in their rituals and alcohol plays a vital role in most modern rites of passage – christenings, weddings and funerals. Alcohol is not just a legally obtainable drug but it is the one psychoactive substance that is regularly sanitized by the political and ecclesiastical establishments. Catholics, protestants and jews all celebrate religious festivals with alcohol. Socially, just about every dinner or toast, speech or public function is celebrated with alcohol. We launch new boats by smashing bottles of champagne over their bows.

This social acceptability means that alcohol is usually the first substance most law-abiding citizens reach for when things start to get tough. In countries throughout the world where powerful and restrictive legislation has been passed to help control substances such as opium, cocaine and cannabis, alcohol is accepted and culturally sanctioned and countless businessmen make entirely legal fortunes out of its production, sale and distribution. In both developed and developing countries the consumption of alcohol is steadily rising. In Europe the sale of cigarettes is worth $47 billion a year while the sale of alcohol is worth over $50 billion a year. In America the comparable figures are $36 billion and $40 billion.

In Britain the ready availability of alcohol in shops and supermarkets has led to a dramatic increase in the incidence of alcoholism among women. A recent survey showed that there are 50,000 women under the age of 30 who are – every day – drinking twice as much as their bodies can cope with – half of all heavily drinking women are single and under the age of 25. Ten years ago there were eight times as many male alcoholics as female alcoholics – today the ratio is down to three to one. One in six women aged between 18 and 24 is drinking dangerously. One in eight women aged 25-34 is drinking too much. The average woman is now drinking over 10 per cent more than she was a decade ago. Most alarming of all, a major study of 18,000 British schoolchildren showed that four out of every ten girls are regular drinkers before they reach the age of eleven. The number of women being admitted to mental hospitals for treatment of alcohol abuse has risen by 25 per cent in the last ten years, while in the same period the number of women dying of alcohol related diseases has gone up by 20 per cent.

There are between nine and ten million alcoholics in America and, according to whose statistics you believe, between three quarters of a million and three million alcoholics in Britain.

The British government's recently introduced Licensing Act (which enables public houses to stay open all day instead of shutting in the afternoons) has increased the availability of the drug.

Most people still believe that the only organ likely to be damaged by drinking alcohol is the liver. It is true that the liver suffers; it does, after all, have the job of getting rid of alcohol that has been drunk. It can cope with small doses but large amounts can cause permanent damage. Most heavy drinkers have livers in which essential cells have already been replaced by fat and long-term drinkers risk developing hepatitis (an inflammation of the liver) or cirrhosis (a badly damaged and scarred condition which can eventually lead to liver failure or death). Someone who drinks regularly and only reasonably heavily is fifteen times as likely to develop cirrhosis as a normal drinker.

Sadly, however, it is not true that the liver is the only organ to suffer. People who drink heavily or steadily or both risk developing cancer, stomach ulcers and muscle wastage as well as liver disease. Heavy drinking irritates the stomach lining, producing chronic indigestion, bleeding and ulcers. There is also an increased risk of developing various nasty types of cancer of the intestinal tract. The pancreas can be badly damaged too. Normally the pancreas gland produces insulin and essential digestive juices, but heavy drinking can lead to chronic pancreatitis – an inflammation of the organ – which can lead to diabetes and severe pain. Half of the people who develop this condition die within five years.

Alcohol can also affect the heart, lungs, bone marrow and sexual organs. Some doctors claim that a small amount of alcohol helps to protect the heart, and I think this is probably true, but all doctors agree that heavy drinking can damage the heart and lead to heart failure and palpitations. Heavy drinking also leads to high blood pressure and that can lead to strokes. People who drink really heavily risk death from respiratory depression – they simply stop breathing because alcohol paralyses the muscles. Alcohol affects the ability of the bone marrow to make new cells and regular drinking can shrink a man's testicles, reduce the size of his penis, cause a loss of pubic hair and make him infertile and impotent.

Women who drink too much run extra risks. Women who get pregnant run a real risk of having backward or low birthweight babies and all women run an increased risk of developing physical problems such as liver disease, for the female body is physiologically more vulnerable than the male body to the adverse effects of alcohol. Women who drink regularly are likely to become menopausal several years early and may gradually acquire a more masculine appearance as their ovaries and sex organs shrink and as their breasts get smaller.

It is, however, the effects that alcohol has on the brain that make it particularly dangerous.

Alcohol is detectable in the brain within half a minute of a glass being emptied and its effect is substantial. Basically, alcohol is a depressant. If you drink a small amount the depressant effect seems to work most noticeably on the part of the brain that controls your tendency to get excited. With the controls depressed you become more excited and talkative. Natural social and personal inhibitions are lifted by alcohol and most people who have a drink or two become looser and less restricted. A quiet individual may become talkative and a shy person may become aggressive. Under the influence of alcohol someone who is normally cautious may stop worrying about what people think. At the same time, the brain's ability to concentrate on information, to understand messages it is receiving and to make judgements on those messages will diminish. Reflexes will go, and although the individual won't be aware of it, the ability to link sensory input to muscular function will be distorted. So the person who has been drinking will think that he or she will be able to talk, dance or drive a car more efficiently than normal whereas, in fact, their ability to do any of these things will be adversely affected.

After just one or two drinks these effects are temporary, but regular drinkers suffer permanent damage. Brain and nervous tissue is damaged with the effect that the memory goes and is replaced by confusion. The ability to think is impaired and fits can occur. Judgement, self-criticism and self-control are all affected. Numbness and tingling of the hands and feet can be accompanied by a constant tremor which appears whenever the blood alcohol level falls and only disappears when more alcohol is consumed. Permanent mental damage – with the victim becoming feeble-minded – is likely after repeated heavy drinking.

The results of all this damage are difficult to overestimate. In France, which has the highest consumption of alcohol per head in the world, and where eight out of ten people think that wine is good for health while one in four think it is quite indispensable, one in ten of all deaths are directly due to the excessive consumption of alcohol. In Britain, where the consumption of alcohol has doubled in the last thirty years, a quarter of the people admitted to hospitals need help because they drink too much. In countries as varied as America, Australia and Argentina, between one third and a half of all the people admitted to psychiatric hospitals need psychiatric in-patient help because of the damage alcohol has done to their brains.

According to the World Health Organization, which has stated that the problems related to alcohol rank among the world's major health problems, alcoholism is now so rife that up to one in ten of the world's people are dependent on alcohol and disabled by drinking. Since an alcoholic is about four times as likely to die in any given year as a non-drinker of the same age, sex and economic status, it is not difficult to see just how dangerous this legally available drug is. And to all these individual health hazards must be added the fact that alcoholics are far more likely to be involved in accidents than non-alcoholics – while every year thousands of perfectly sober citizens are killed by car drivers who are under the influence of alcohol.

Alcohol causes between a third and a half of all road deaths in developed countries. It causes about a third of all accidents at work. It is involved in a third of all divorces and a third of all child abuse cases. One in ten men admit that their work is being affected by their drinking and millions of working days are lost each year through alcohol abuse. In America more than 75 per cent of all police time is spent on alcohol-related crimes and about one half of all murders are alcohol-related, in that either the victim or the murderer had been drinking. In Britain research reported in the *British Journal of Addiction* showed that 64 per cent of all people arrested had been drinking in the four hours prior to their arrest while among people arrested between 10 p.m. and 2 a.m. 93 per cent had been drinking heavily. Among the under-18-year-olds arrested, 65 per cent had been drinking. Alcohol is a significant factor in about 1,000 arrests every day in Britain. Two out of every five fires in Britain are caused by someone who is drunk. One in five people who drown is drunk. A third of all industrial accidents are caused by alcohol. At least one thousand children and young people are killed by alcohol every year in Britain (making alcohol the main killer of young children in the country). Two out of three attempted suicides are linked to alcohol. The damage done by alcohol in Britain is estimated to cost well over a billion pounds a year.

Most people who become addicted to alcohol start by drinking socially but quickly learn that alcohol provides some relief from stress and day-to-day psychological problems. As a result alcohol becomes a regular crutch. The rate at which problems start to arise depends upon the age and sex of the individual, his or her family history (there is a hereditary factor involved and if both your parents were alcoholics then you have an increased risk of becoming an alcoholic yourself) and the amount of pressure the individual is under.

The budding alcoholic starts drinking secretly, feeling guilty about his drinking and drinking in the mornings as well as the evenings. He will need to increase his intake of alcohol in order to survive comfortably. He may well keep on drinking until he gets physically sick. By this time he will have developed a tremendous tolerance to alcohol and will be able to drink enormous quantities of it without any apparent effect.

Gradually, the alcoholic's home and work life begins to suffer. His failures at home and at work will make him aggressive and resentful. When he loses friends, get thrown out of home or is fired from work, he will feel aggrieved and drink more and more in order to try to cope. It is at this point that he may become violent, physically attacking his wife or children. Wife and baby battering are a common consequence of alcoholism in men.

The alcoholic is likely to smell of alcohol at odd times of day, although he may try to disguise this by using a powerful aftershave. (Women alcoholics have an advantage here for they can douse themselves in perfume.) The alcoholic will probably have a regular hand tremor that makes it difficult for him to write legibly and he will probably develop chronic indigestion. He will worry if he has not got supplies at hand and will keep stores of his favourite beverage hidden in drawers and cupboards, frequently drinking alone and in secret. Alcoholics frequently lie about their drinking habits (just as all drug addicts do) and may start stealing in order to pay for supplies.

In the final stages the alcoholic will drink for days at a time, get completely drunk and stay that way. He won't bother eating properly and will take no care of his physical appearance. He will suffer from terrible tremors and as his liver begins to stop working properly his tolerance to alcohol will disappear and he will need smaller and smaller amounts to get drunk.

As soon as the alcoholic tries to manage without a drink he will start to suffer withdrawal symptoms. Within six to eight hours of stopping drinking he will start to sweat and feel sick. His limbs will tremble and he will be confused, disorientated, restless, frightened and paranoid. He will probably have hallucinations (imagining that he can see rats, spiders, toads, snakes or demons) and begin shaking. He may become violent and there is a good chance that he will start having fits. These symptoms can last for several days.

Every piece of available evidence shows quite clearly that alcohol is one of the most potentially dangerous and addictive drugs known. And yet alcohol is sold in supermarkets and corner shops alongside bread and fruit and it is advertized on television and in magazines. In America and Europe alcohol companies spend around $6 billion a year on advertizing and sponsorship. Not long ago the British Medical Association abandoned its attempt to call for a total ban on advertizing alcohol when it realized that this would mean that it would have to close down its own Wine Club for doctors. In Britain the production, marketing and selling of alcoholic drinks employs over three quarters of a million people and alcohol exports earn the country over £1,000 million a year. In some countries the figures are even more astonishing. In France, for example, something like ten per cent of the entire workforce earn their living in the production and sale of alcohol. In developing countries the establishment of a brewing industry is often one of the first steps towards industrialization (as the locals are encouraged to give up chewing leaves or drinking stimulating herb teas and start drinking whisky or gin instead).

The final irony is the fact that millions of people who would not dream of smoking a marijuana cigarette, chewing a coca leaf or smoking an opium pipe will happily buy alcohol by the crateful and think nothing of getting legless every Saturday night. The laws which differentiate between illegal drugs such as cannabis and cocaine and legal drugs such as alcohol are largely responsible for the feeling that alcoholic drinks cannot possibly be all that dangerous since they are, after all, widely available.

Tobacco

The smoking of tobacco is said to have started when Christopher Columbus received a gift of tobacco leaves from the natives of San Salvador and brought them back to Europe. Throughout the seventeenth century tobacco gradually grew in popularity, mainly as a medicine that could be relied upon to cure just about anything from deafness to headaches to flushes. To begin with, most people chewed tobacco; the idea of smoking the leaves was popularized by the Turks during the Crimean War.

By the end of the nineteenth century there were roughly equal numbers of people chewing and smoking tobacco in both Britain and America but the production of the first machine-rolled cigarettes revolutionized tobacco habits throughout the world. By the end of the First World War in 1918 (during which, incidentally, the British army distributed cigarettes to its soldiers, thereby probably doing as much harm to some of them as the German army was doing) more people were smoking than chewing and cigarettes had overtaken pipes in popularity. The introduction of machine-rolled cigarettes had one other major effect – women started smoking. The cigarette is a perfect example of how science and industry have together turned a relatively harmless pastime (chewing tobacco leaves) into a dangerous addiction. Modern cigarettes are perfectly designed to ensure that the dangerous substances cigarettes contain are directed into the body quickly, repeatedly and conveniently.

Once fairly large numbers of people started smoking tobacco, it quickly became clear that some were getting addicted. In the 1890s there were already companies selling products such as NO-TO-BAC to help smokers give up the habit. As tobacco rose in popularity many scientists started to investigate its properties and in 1928 researchers isolated nicotine and identified it as an active ingredient of tobacco. They also found that it was a particularly poisoning substance: there is enough nicotine in the average cigar to kill two people and the only reason why cigars and cigarettes are not instantly lethal is that the nicotine they contain is taken into the body fairly slowly.

Writing in the *Journal of the American Medical Association*, William Pollin, the director of the United States National Institute of Drug Abuse, reported that nicotine is six or eight times more addictive than alcohol; and Dr Jack Heningfield of the National Institute of Drug Abuse's Addiction Research Centre has claimed that nicotine is between five and ten times as potent as cocaine.

Apart from its poisonous qualities, nicotine has a number of undesirable effects on the human body. It stimulates the central nervous system and increases the electrical activity of the brain, lowers the skin temperature, causes blood vessels in the skin to become narrow, increases the blood pressure and the heart rate and numbs the taste buds. Cigarette smoke also contains several thousand other poisonous substances: for example, carbon monoxide gas which reduces the oxygen-carrying capacity of the blood and is one of the main reasons why heavy smokers so often complain of a shortness of breath. Other chemicals contained in tobacco cause cancer and the list of diseases associated with smoking grows annually. Smokers are vulnerable to respiratory disorders such as asthma and bronchitis, to chest infections, sinus troubles, indigestion, gastritis and peptic ulcers. Many circulatory problems, raised blood pressure, arterial blockages and strokes are all known to be tobacco-related. There is a strong link between smoking and heart disease and smokers are twice as likely to die of heart disease as are non-smokers. Finally, there is lung cancer, the disease most commonly associated with cigarettes. Altogether there can be absolutely no doubt that tobacco is considerably more harmful – both qualitatively and quantitatively – than heroin, cocaine or cannabis.

According to official statistics the majority of the thousands of people who have major surgery in Britain are smokers; 95 per cent of all patients with serious arterial disease of the legs are smokers and 20 per cent of the 180,000 people who die of coronary artery disease every year in Britain do so because they smoke. The Chief Medical Officer at the Department of Social

Legal drugs and their dangers

Security in Britain has described smoking as 'by far the largest avoidable hazard to health' and 'the most lethal instrument devised by man for peaceful use'. Around 100,000 Britons are killed every year because they smoked cigarettes, while exhaled cigarette smoke kills around 1,000 non-smokers a year – mainly through various types of cancer and heart disease.

Moreover, at a world conference on lung health in Boston in 1990, Dr Stanton Glantz of the University of California in San Francisco estimated that passive smoking (the cigarette smoke inhaled by non-smokers) kills 50,000 Americans a year – two thirds of whom die of heart disease. That is, without a doubt, far, far more than the number of people who die from using *all* illegal drugs. According to the World Health Organization, tobacco smoke in the environment is responsible for around one quarter of all the lung cancers which affect non-smokers. A WHO statement published in May 1991 warned that 'in marriages where one partner smokes and the other does not, the risk of lung cancer to the non-smoker is 20-50 per cent higher'.

Cigarettes are also a major cause of fire. In America, for example, cigarettes are cited as the main cause of residential fires. (It is interesting to note that legally obtainable alcohol and tobacco are together responsible for the deaths of many thousands of non-users every year, whereas users of illegal substances such as cannabis, cocaine and heroin are responsible for a negligible number of non-user deaths).

In America the Surgeon General claims that tobacco is responsible for around a third of a million deaths every year and the cost of cigarette smoking in America has been estimated at over $40 billion. In May 1991 the World Health Organization claimed that 'tobacco will cause about three million deaths a year throughout the world in the 1990s, including one million in the developing countries'.

Despite all this well documented and well publicized evidence, and despite the printing of health warnings on cigarette packs and cigarette advertizements, countless millions around the world continue to smoke. The vast majority smoke because they are addicted. Despite the fact that when smokers give up their habit they suffer clear withdrawal symptoms such as anxiety and restlessness there has, in the past, been a considerable amount of argument about whether or not people do get addicted to tobacco. It has, however, been shown that if smokers are given low-nicotine cigarettes to replace their normal brand they will tend to smoke more of the low-nicotine cigarettes. This evidence supports the theory that smokers can become addicted to tobacco – and its ingredients. Virtually the only people who no longer believe that tobacco is addictive are the people selling cigarettes. In May 1990 a spokesman for B.A.T. (one of the world's largest tobacco companies) was quoted in the London *Sunday Times* as denying that smoking was addictive. He gave as supporting evidence the fact that thousands of people give up smoking every year. On this basis there can be little doubt that heroin, cocaine and cannabis are not addictive either.

Despite – or possibly because of – the publicity about the dangers of tobacco smoking, and the protests from those who object to the pollution of the atmosphere, the number of people smoking remains high. In Britain, for example, about one adult in three still smokes, one quarter of fifteen-year-olds are regular smokers and one third of teenagers are smoking by the age of nineteen. One reason for this is undoubtedly the skill with which the tobacco companies plan their marketing campaigns and promote their products. For every ten people who give up smoking, eight or nine non-smokers take up the habit.

Tobacco companies spend around $700 million a year on tobacco advertizing in America and around $1 billion a year in Europe. If sponsorship and other promotional activities are included the total figure doubles. The alcohol industry is now the fastest growing sponsor of sporting events but tobacco companies have for years used sports sponsorship as a way of obtaining television coverage. The tobacco industry has to recruit 300 new smokers every day just to replace the ones it has killed.

All around the world attempts are being made to introduce more and more rules to control the advertizing of tobacco, but the tobacco companies are powerful and are fighting hard. Tobacco companies and their agencies have commissioned studies which show that advertizing has no impact on total cigarette sales but merely persuades people to switch brands. M.J. Waterson, research director of the Advertising Association in Britain, was one of the first to offer this argument in 1981 in a booklet entitled 'Advertising and Cigarette Consumption'. Waterson claimed that advertizing expenditure had not had any significant influence on the total size of the cigarette market for twenty years and claimed that 'advertising does not stimulate or maintain cigarette consumption levels'. He concluded that 'a cigarette advertising ban would be both futile and damaging to the interests of the consumer'.

The World Health Organization has never found this argument convincing. In 1982 its Expert Committee on Smoking Control Strategies in Developing Countries reported that 'some pro-smoking advertizements do not even mention a brand name' and that 'tobacco companies enjoying a complete monopoly in a country none the less advertize'. More recently the New Zealand Toxic Substance Board, which has examined the link between advertizing and smoking in 33 countries between 1970 and 1986, has shown that in countries with a total ban on tobacco advertizing the consumption of tobacco falls steadily, whereas in countries where there are no restrictions the annual consumption of tobacco rises steadily. However, despite the evidence many governments are still reluctant to upset the tobacco companies or to risk losing their tax revenues from the sale of cigarettes. In 1991 the European Parliament voted on a total ban on tobacco advertizing in all types of media but Britain, West Germany, Denmark and Holland opposed it.

Perhaps this is not as surprising as it sounds. Although the European Community spends around £7 million a year campaigning against smoking, it provides its tobacco growers with a subsidy of around £870 million a year. Tobacco is the most heavily subsidized commodity of the EC's Common Agricultural policy. It does seem obscenely hypocritical that countries which spend such huge amounts of money fighting the distribution and use of relatively harmless drugs such as cannabis should actually support the production of a far more dangerous substance which is directly responsible for millions of deaths a year.

The final outrage, however, is probably the fact that as the western, developed countries struggle hard to oppose the power of the international tobacco companies, and to ensure that the marketing and advertizing of tobacco is stopped, the directors of many tobacco companies are starting to sell their products in the developing countries where controls are at a minimum and where cigarettes can be sold with advertizements which take full advantage of local fears and ambitions. Tobacco advertizements in Third World countries carry no health warnings and advertizements are used that would not be allowed in countries where those companies are based. The moral shortcomings of the world's tobacco companies are no less obvious than the moral shortcomings of the world's cocaine and heroin dealers.

Caffeine

Alcohol and tobacco are the most obvious and most widely used legally available addictive drugs. But they certainly are not the only addictive – and potentially harmful – substances in common usage.

Caffeine is probably the most widely used and most underestimated drug in the world today. The annual worldwide consumption of coffee is about 5 million tonnes. Drinks containing caffeine have been consumed for centuries. Coffee was first exported from Ethiopia in the sixth century and tea was considered powerful enough to be used as a medicine in the fourth century.

Despite its wide availability caffeine is a remarkably powerful stimulant: it stimulates the brain and nervous system; it increases the effect of acid on the stomach; it makes the heart beat faster and pushes up the blood pressure; it opens up the lungs and it stimulates the kidneys. Too much caffeine can lead to muscle tremors, insomnia, anxiety, depression, headaches, indigestion, palpitations, bowel problems and personality changes. And there is no doubt at all that caffeine is addictive. Many people cannot start the day without a cup of coffee or tea and regular users who want to cut down are usually advised to do so slowly in order to avoid the unpleasant effects of sudden withdrawal – headaches, depression, anxiety and irritability being the commonest.

Caffeine almost certainly causes more physical and mental problems than the use of illegal drugs such as cannabis. The symptoms caused by caffeine overdosage are likely to develop in adults when the daily intake exceeds 250 mg and in children when the daily intake exceeds 125 mg. It is not difficult to exceed these levels: a cup of ground coffee contains between 100 and 150 mg of caffeine; a cup of instant coffee contains between 75 and 100 mg; a cup of tea contains between 50 and 100 mg; a mug of cocoa contains about 50mg; and cola drinks often contain 50 mg of caffeine.

There are, without a doubt, millions of caffeine addicts in Britain. Most never realize that they feel ill because of the caffeine they are taking. Because they never need do without their daily fix, the withdrawal symptoms are never particularly severe. Anyone who ever develops a headache after an hour or two without a drink of coffee or a cup of tea, who feels uncomfortable when waking up in the morning and cannot get going without a caffeine 'fix', or who suffers from any of the symptoms I have described as being associated with the over-use of caffeine, is probably addicted and should consider cutting down, either by drinking weaker coffee or tea or by drinking fewer cups.

But these are not the only consequences of regular caffeine use. Numerous scientific research studies have shown that caffeine-containing beverages can be dangerous. After a critical assessment of a large number of experimental and epidemiological studies, the International Agency for Research on Cancer recently concluded that coffee may cause bladder cancer, while drinking tea may increase the risk of oesophageal cancer. It is worth pointing out that no one has yet seriously suggested that heroin, cocaine or cannabis are linked to the development of cancer of any kind.

Steroids

The type of substance to which individuals can become addicted varies enormously and can be dependent upon a huge variety of factors including social circumstances, environment and personal ambitions. Athletes and body builders, for example, frequently get hooked on steroids. A few years ago 198 world class athletes were asked if they would take pills that guaranteed them an Olympic gold medal even if they knew that the pills would kill them within five years. Incredibly, 103 of the athletes said that they would take the pills and accept the risks. Today the use of drugs by international athletes is widely accepted; those who are found out are expected to serve a short period in the sporting wilderness but the publicity they get will probably mean that their earning power goes up rather than down.

━━━ Glue sniffing

Among school-children glue sniffing is popular; probably because glue is fairly cheap to buy and easy to obtain. In Britain the Department of Education and Science estimated in the 1980s that ten per cent of British children aged between 12 and 17 had experimented with glue sniffing. Proving that whenever there is a demand there will always be a supplier, a shopkeeper in Scotland was arrested for selling children a special glue sniffing kit which consisted of glue and plastic bags from which to inhale the fumes. Those who regard glue sniffing as a relatively minor problem (and many doctors, school teachers and social workers have dismissed it as a rather insignificant hazard) should know that in *Drugs of Abuse: An Introduction to Their Actions and Potential Hazards* Dr Samuel Irwin ranks glue sniffing as more dangerous than using amphetamines, barbiturates, heroin, marijuana or hallucinogens such as LSD. The statistics show that glue sniffing has been responsible for a number of deaths and many cases of permanent physical damage. Between 1971 and 1983, 236 children died from glue sniffing in Britain. In Japan there were 161 deaths from glue sniffing in one year alone. Glue has killed more people than cocaine and cannabis combined. By the time a young glue user shows such clear symptoms as weight loss, moodiness, inattentiveness, drowsiness, unusual irritability, tremor, persistent headaches, sores or rashes around his mouth or nose, running eyes, a cough and the general symptoms of a persistent cold, he is likely to be addicted.

Addiction to food

If we define a drug of addiction as a substance that some people cannot control once they start taking it – even though they know it is making them ill and ruining their life – then food has to be the commonest of all addictions. Around the world tens of millions of people are grossly overweight, dramatically increasing their chances of suffering from heart disease and a score of other potentially crippling disorders. It is impossible to say precisely how many people have died because of their addiction to food but the total figure must make food as big a killer as tobacco. Together those two perfectly legal addictions have probably killed a thousand times more people than all illegal drugs combined.

Most people who are overweight are constantly trying – and failing – to lose weight. At any one time eight out of ten women are on a diet or are about to start one. Sadly, it is widely accepted that nine out of ten would-be slimmers will fail to maintain their weight loss. Some individuals are addicted to particular types of food. Chocolate, which contains phenylethylamine – structurally similar to the amphetamines – is one of the most commonly abused foodstuffs. Sugar, a relatively useless foodstuff, is consumed by the tonne by people who are addicted to it. Others are just addicted to food in general and will eat anything they can find.

We are all conditioned to eat for a variety of reasons which have nothing to do with hunger. Most slimming experts agree that boredom, loneliness and anxiety are common causes of overeating. These are, of course, common causes of all kinds of drug abuse. Like all addicts, food addicts lie both to themselves and to their friends. 'I hardly ever eat anything', 'I have a hormonal problem' and 'I only have to look at a cake to put on weight' are three common lies. People over-eat (and under-eat) to take control of their own lives, to punish themselves, to defend themselves, to give themselves an excuse for social failure, to help themselves 'escape' from a world in which they feel uncomfortable and to give themselves comfort. These are all common reasons for all types of drug addiction.

The Drugs Myth

Not all addicts are addicted to substances; many are addicted to types of behaviour. Some people are addicted to gambling; others get addicted to work, to shopping, to playing arcade machines, to falling in love (the symptoms of being in love – dry mouth, racing heart, sweating, trembling, insomnia, anorexia and an inability to concentrate are similar to the symptoms of drug use and withdrawal) or to exercise. Thousands are addicted to behavioural patterns which seem bizarre to say the least. According to Susie Orbach, author of *Fat is a Feminist Issue*, one third of women in their late teens and early twenties control their weight by vomiting, by fasting or by taking laxatives or diuretics.

Prescription drugs

I cannot possibly end this chapter dealing with legal addictions without referring to the millions of patients who get hooked on perfectly legal prescription drugs, and showing how doctors and drug companies together combine to originate and perpetuate drug abuse of the fiercest and most damaging kind. The careless, indiscriminate and virtually criminal over-prescribing of amphetamines, bromides, barbiturates and a hundred other drug groups have led to widespread drug addiction, enormous amounts of agony and numerous deaths.

As long ago as the early 1950s it was clear the addiction of patients to barbiturates was more serious than the addiction of patients to morphine. At the United States Public Health Services Addiction Research Center in Lexington, Kentucky, research workers did some important work with volunteers which showed that after taking the drug for a mere three months, withdrawal produced psychoses, epileptic convulsions and other serious symptoms. In 1972 in Britain the barbiturates were blamed for 1,000 suicide deaths and in America in the 1970s the barbiturates were said to be killing 10,000 people a year. In 1978 the number of prescriptions being written for barbiturates in Britain was down to 5,000,000 a year but the government had still not taken action to control prescribing patterns. By 1984 the number of barbiturate prescriptions written for patients who had never previously taken the drug was down to 76,000 and in January 1985, when the problem was more or less under control, the government in Britain finally and belatedly brought the barbiturates under the prescribing requirements of the Misuse of Drugs Act 1973.

The virtual disappearance of the barbiturates was, I suspect, greeted with some enthusiasm by the manufacturers of benzodiazepines, another group of drugs which were recommended for similar symptoms – particularly anxiety and sleeplessness – and which were said to be perfectly safe. The resultant over-prescribing of the benzodiazepines has created problems which have vastly overshadowed the problems created by the barbiturates. The benzodiazepines are probably the most addictive drugs ever created and the vast army of enthusiastic doctors who prescribed these drugs by the tonne have created the world's largest drug addiction problem. I am well aware of the size of this problem because I have been campaigning to persuade politicians and doctors to control the benzodiazepines more effectively for most of my professional life; during that time I have heard from and spoken to tens of thousands of addicts whose lives have been ruined by these drugs.

I first became aware of the size of the problem associated with the benzodiazepines back in 1973. At the time I was spending part of my week in the midlands where I worked as a part-time assistant in general practice, and part of it in London where I worked as executive editor of the *British Clinical Journal*, a new monthly medical magazine.

While I had been at medical school I had been painfully aware of the power of the drugs industry and my early experiences in hospital and general practices had convinced me that the major drug companies had far too much control over medical education and over doctors' prescribing habits. My anxiety about the techniques used by some of the large drug companies had already caused some controversy. In 1972 I had written an article for the *Daily Telegraph* in London entitled 'Hard Sell in the Surgery', in which I had complained about the marketing techniques used to sell drugs such as sedatives and tranquillizers. As a result of that one article, one drug company executive told the publisher of the Journal I was editing that his company would only buy advertizing space if I was 'controlled' more effectively or, better still, sacked.

But I was not sacked (and I was not controlled either) and in April 1973, on behalf of the Journal, I helped to organize a symposium at the Royal Society of Medicine in London entitled: 'The Uses and Limitations of Psychotropic Drugs in General Practice'.

The subject of the benzodiazepines came up about halfway through the meeting and the critical comment that made me sit up came from Dr John Bonn who was, at the time, a senior lecturer and consultant psychiatrist at St Bartholomew's and Hackney Hospitals in London. Bonn pointed out that he regularly saw benzodiazepine-dependent patients coming to be taken off their drugs and said that he considered that the drugs should only be used on patients who were under close supervision:

> When patients are taken off benzodiazepines successfully, many of them say that they feel better than they have felt for years, without any further treatment. The danger of the benzodiazepines is insidious. These drugs have withdrawal effects very similar to those of barbiturates and alcohol but these withdrawal effects may take much longer to come on.

This was, remember, 1973 and copies of the *British Clinical Journal* in which that symposium appeared were sent to most if not all British general practitioners.

But it was known long before this that the benzodiazepines caused problems. The first scientific paper showing that they could be addictive was published in 1961 – just a year after chlordiazepoxide (the first of the benzodiazepines) had been launched in America. The first clinical report I have been able to find that detailed the addictive qualities of the benzodiazepines was published in a journal called *Psychopharmacologia*. It was written by three doctors from the Veterans' Administration Hospital in Palo Alto, California. The paper was entitled 'Withdrawal Reactions from Chlordiazepoxide' and it described in dramatic detail how patients who had been taking the drug suffered from withdrawal symptoms when the drug was stopped. This paper was published nine years before I qualified as a doctor and twelve years before Dr John Bonn spoke at the symposium I have described.

The authors of the paper published in *Psychopharmacologia* described how eleven patients who had been taking fairly high doses of chlordiazepoxide for up to six months were suddenly taken off their pills and given sugar tablets instead. Ten of the eleven patients experienced new symptoms after withdrawal. Six patients became depressed, five were agitated and unable to sleep. Two of the patients had major convulsions or fits. Most of the symptoms developed within two to nine days after the drug was stopped. By the early 1970s a number of other papers had been published showing that the benzodiazepines could cause addiction. In 1975 the *International Journal of the Addictions* carried a major article entitled 'Misuse and Abuse of Diazepam: An Increasingly Common Medical Problem'.

In 1975 my first book, *The Medicine Men*, was published. Here is what I wrote about the benzodiazepine tranquillizers:

There is little doubt that many of the least necessary prescriptions are for psychotropic drugs. Something like 17 per cent of all prescriptions signed in America in 1970 were for psychotropic drugs, and in the United Kingdom the figure for the same year was nearer to 19 per cent. The percentage seems to be rising annually and there is little doubt that psychotropic drugs are becoming increasingly popular. The total cost of the 47 million prescriptions handed out for psychotropic drugs in England and Wales in 1970 was over £20 million. It has been estimated that over 3,000 million psychotropic tablets are dispensed every year in England and Wales. The market for these drugs, given for the sole purpose of helping patients who are anxious or depressed or who are unable to get to sleep at night, is so enormous and is growing so rapidly that almost every manufacturer of drugs in the world produces its share of psychotropic drugs. People who insist that they would not normally take tablets of any kind and who condemn those who take cannabis or alcohol, happily take psychotropics, with the result that the world's biggest addiction problem is not teenagers taking hash but middle-agers taking sedatives.

The Drugs Myth

People in responsible positions, outwardly well adjusted and in control, live on regular daily doses of drugs designed to help them cope with their problems. Journalists, bus conductors, housewives and school teachers all swallow their capsules three times a day without regret. It has been said that if all the people on psychotropics were banned from driving or operating machinery, the world's economy would collapse. The tranquilliser is replacing tobacco. It will perhaps give us an even bigger problem. It may prove even more dangerous. Already Valium is said to be taken by 14 per cent of the population in Britain, 17 per cent in Belgium and France, 15 per cent in Denmark, 10 per cent in Italy and Spain, 14 per cent in Germany and 10 per cent in America.

The habit usually starts insidiously. The patient may have a good excuse for taking a few tablets. A close friend or relative has died or there is a rush on at work. And the doctor finds it difficult to refuse the request for a little help. Both patient and doctor forget that anxiety and depression are normal, healthy human emotions. The drugs which people take to help relieve their pressures vary. If he is young the addict may take drugs from a pusher. If he is older he may take drugs from a medical adviser.

That, remember, was published in 1975.

Over the following years I wrote dozens of newspaper and magazine articles on the subject of benzodiazepine addiction and I helped to make scores of television and radio programmes. As a result I received tens of thousands of letters from tranquillizer users (at one time I was getting well over a thousand letters a week from people who were hooked on tranquillizers and who wanted help). By the early 1980s I estimated that there were between two-and-a-half and three million benzodiazepine addicts in Britain – and millions more around the world. In addition to the letters from patients I also received a vast number of letters from doctors, for although tens of thousands of doctors were still handing out benzodiazepines freely a growing number were becoming aware of the problem. Many consultants and general practitioners wrote to tell me that they thought that the benzodiazepines were the most addictive drugs in common use and countless drug experts told me that in their experience patients found it far harder to get off the benzodiazepines than off any illegal drugs.

Eventually, in January 1988 the Committee on Safety of Medicines finally issued a warning headed 'Benzodiazepine dependence and withdrawal symptoms'. The warning advised doctors that the benzodiazepines should not be used for more than four weeks, and warned that long-term chronic use was not recommended. On March 1st 1988, speaking at the twenty-eighth sitting of Standing Committee A on the Health and Medicines Bill at the House of Commons in London, Mrs Edwina Currie, Parliamentary Secretary for Health, replying to questions about the benzodiazepines, said:

> We have taken action because I have been worried about the problem. Dr Vernon Coleman's articles, to which I refer with approval, raised concern about these important matters and I sent them on to the appropriate bodies.

By then it was too late for millions of patients. The government, the drug industry and the medical profession should have acted fifteen years earlier – when the evidence they needed was first made available. The medical profession had created the biggest drug addiction problem to originate in the twentieth century. Sadly, even today, three years after that official announcement, I am still getting letters every day from British patients who are being given benzodiazepine tranquillizers and translations of my articles and books about benzodiazepines have shown that the benzodiazepine problem is only just emerging in many other countries.

Most alarming of all, perhaps, is the fact that the medical profession, the politicians and the drug companies seem to have learned little or nothing from the tragic benzodiazepine story.

Consider, for example, the drug buspirone which was launched in January 1988 – the same month that the Committee on Safety of Medicines in Britain published its warning about the benzodiazepines.

When buspirone was launched a writer in *The Times* described the drug as an alternative to the benzodiazepines and a spokesman for Bristol-Myers, the international drug company which had developed buspirone was reported to have claimed that the drug was 'effective without being addictive'. The science correspondent of *The Times* told his readers that the drug aimed 'to avoid addiction problems which affect about one million patients'.

But my investigations made me very sceptical. A few days' research convinced me that the company making the drug would *not* know for certain whether or not their product was entirely safe and entirely non-addictive until thousands of ordinary people had tried it.

I firmly believe that any drug prescribed for anxiety will eventually prove to be addictive, but it seems to me that neither doctors nor drug companies are prepared to abandon the search for a profitable pharmacological solution to anxiety. The result is, I fear, that in the future the problems associated with the benzodiazepines will be repeated time and time again. The benzodiazepines have caused infinitely more sorrow and despair than all illegal drugs put together and yet governments and legislators have been so busy concentrating on the control of illegal drugs such as heroin, cocaine and cannabis that they have consistently failed to act and protect patients until enormous amounts of unnecessary damage have been done. Effective controls on the barbiturates came a decade too late and the significant warning about the benzodiazepines also came well over a decade too late. Politicians and legislators have presumably assumed that because a drug is available on prescription it must be safe. If they had put one per cent of the effort that has gone into an attempt to halt illegal drug smuggling into controlling the promotion and prescribing of the benzodiazepines the public would have benefited beyond all measure.

The drugs war

Despite the obvious hypocrisy, the governments of numerous developed countries have for decades been attempting to control the production, sale and use of a relatively small number of drugs through the introduction and prosecution of an apparently unending series of laws.

The first international body to be concerned with the control of narcotic drugs was the International Opium Commission, which met in Shanghai in 1909 and consisted of representatives from thirteen countries. Their deliberations led to the signing (at The Hague) of the first modern drug control treaty: the International Opium Convention of 1912, which established international co-operation in the control of narcotic drugs as a matter of law.

Unfortunately, it always takes time to get international treaties signed and ratified and intentions often prove to be impracticably enthusiastic. By 1914, when the First World War broke out, only six countries had signed the treaty.

At the end of the war the peace treaty included signature of the Hague Convention, but it quickly became clear that too many people were ignoring this and so, during the early post-war years, the League of Nations created an Opium Advisory Committee. At a convention held in Geneva in 1925 another piece of legislation was introduced which was intended to be more practical, more positive and more powerful. The 1925 legislation included cannabis for reasons which I have already explained: it had absolutely nothing to do with science or logic but a lot to do with politics.

The Drugs Myth

Unfortunately, the price the legislators paid was far too high and the inclusion of cannabis as a 'dangerous, narcotic drug' has weakened all subsequent legislation. Drug users, doctors and even policemen who all know that cannabis is a remarkably innocuous substance are either confused by the legislation, or else they simply find it difficult to show it the proper respect.

Since the 1925 convention was signed a number of other drug control conferences have been held and a vast number of other treaties and conventions have been signed. After the Second World War the United Nations took over the functions of the League of Nations and the World Health Organization became involved. In 1948 new legislation brought a number of synthetic substances under control (prior to that the only drugs considered illegal were products of three plants: the opium poppy, the coca bush and the cannabis plant) and in 1971 yet another convention extended the international drug control system to cover hallucinogens such as LSD, sedatives, hypnotics such as the barbiturates and stimulants such as the amphetamines.

Today the legal control of drug use is unbelievably complicated. The United Nations has a number of drug control organizations and every individual country has its own laws and its own drug enforcement agencies. Britain, for example, has introduced over forty separate laws to control the use of drugs in the last one hundred years. In the first half of 1988 245 of the 1099 bills before the American House of Representatives dealt with drugs – calling for stricter penalties (including the death penalty) for drug pushers, mandatory drug testing for ordinary citizens and greater rights for law enforcement agencies. While politicians take up their time discussing the problem of how to win the drugs war, roads crumble, hospitals close and the environment becomes dirtier.

Inevitably, laws vary enormously from one country to another. For example, at the last count thirteen countries had the death penalty for possessing or selling heroin and six countries had the death penalty for possessing or selling cannabis. Japan's first drug control laws were introduced in 1870 and included decapitation with a samurai sword as the punishment for drug smuggling and today the Japanese are still extremely critical of what they regard as 'soft' or 'lenient' policies in many other countries – particularly toward drug users, who the Japanese punish almost as severely as they punish drug pushers. They believe that the user is as worthy of punishment as the supplier since without the user there would be no supplier. A simple argument which may be crudely logical, and which is supported vociferously by the drug producing nations who claim that control of those who use and buy drugs would automatically eliminate all sources of supply, but which does lack understanding or compassion.

In China drug dealers can be – and often are – executed after mass sentencing rallies in sports stadiums while addicts who refuse to change their evil ways can be sent to labour camps without trial for up to three years. These barbaric attitudes are not particularly effective, however, and those who smuggle drugs can be just as barbaric. One Burmese drug baron had a man he suspected of being a government informant buried alive as an example to other villagers. Another suspected informant was hung, drawn and quartered in the main village street. Up until very recently a member of the Yakuza – a Japanese version of the Mafia – who made a mistake was expected to chop off his own finger and offer it to his godfather. If the 'gift' was accepted then this was regarded as a sign that he would be forgiven. This practice is now discouraged since the Japanese gangsters have discovered that without their fingers their golf game suffers.

Ironically, although westerners are often vociferous in their demand for tougher drug laws, public opinion is often aroused by sympathy when westerners are arrested smuggling drugs in countries where the punishments are severe. Even the fiercest of penalties seem to make no difference, however. In Iran, where there are estimated to be around three million heroin addicts – one in twelve of the population – the Ayatollah Khalkhali had to repeal the death penalty he had introduced for drug addicts when it became clear that he would probably end up executing one twelfth of his country's population. In the Middle East alcohol is forbidden by drug control laws but westerners smuggle alcohol in or distil their own illegally and think nothing of it because alcohol is not an illegal drug in their own countries (some westerners admit that the very illegality makes alcohol use more exciting).

The World Health Organization recently published a very brief and superficial summary of the international legislation covering the forms of treatment available in different countries. The publication takes up 82 pages and deals only with legislation governing the *treatment* of drug addicts. To enforce all these complex, individual laws all countries have their own enforcement agencies. In most countries everything is made even more complicated (and expensive) by the fact that different agencies are involved. Inevitably, there are jealousies and demarcation disputes and the squabbles between competing agencies frequently create even more confusion and many inconsistencies.

In America, in particular, the competition between agencies has been tremendous and the habit of separate drug enforcement agencies claiming the same drug seizures to their own credit has frequently led to totally unreliable estimates of the total weight of drugs intercepted. In one recent year, for example, the US customs included a seizure of 3906 pounds of cocaine in their figures and so did the Drug Enforcement Administration. Because there are (or were at the latest count) eleven federal agencies in the United States of America involved in the prosecution of drug offenders, one package of cannabis can be counted eleven times by people wanting bigger grants and more power for their own agency. Similarly, the number of addicts using drugs and the numbers arrested are invariably and inevitably exaggerated.

Despite criticism from many countries that American legislation is too weak, there are powerful voices who believe firmly that the laws in America are too restrictive. In his book *Drug Use and Abuse*, British drugs expert Dr James Willis claimed that 'repressive anti-drug legislation in the United States of America has contributed to a major social disaster by intensifying the problems of criminality'.

In the end there can be no doubt that the differences between attitudes in the various countries around the world leads to confusion, inefficiency and unfairness – and, at times, to bizarre consequences. In the 1960s the French regarded heroin as an essentially American problem and were not particularly interested in doing anything about its passage through their country. This attitude changed when a glut of heroin appeared on the streets of Paris and the local problem intensified. The Central Intelligence Agency in America has denied allegations that the heroin was planted in Paris by them to help encourage the French to take the problem more seriously.

Around the world the cost of the drugs 'war' has been steadily increasing for years. At the start of the 1980s the United States spent over $1 billion a year on its drugs war. During the 1980s they quadrupled their expenditure but the prices of drugs fell and the number of users went up. In 1988 the House of Representatives moved $475 million from the star wars budget into the budget allocated to help interrupt the drug supply and suggested putting the armed services in charge of stopping drug trafficking. The amount of effort put into the drugs war has always been vastly greater than the effort put into preventing or treating drug problems and there is no immediate sign that this will change since politicians, legislators and law enforcement agencies seem to see the 'war' as the only option.

And yet the drugs war has been laughably inefficient. A decade or so ago most drugs were 'body-packed' across borders. Smugglers would put cocaine into balloons or condoms and then swallow them. This technique was dangerous for if a condom or balloon burst the smuggler would probably die. But the risks were considered worthwhile by men and women who knew that one trip could make them rich. Today, most drugs are smuggled by aeroplane (something like 80 per cent of the cocaine used in America comes from one group of Colombian gangsters). Sometimes an aeroplane will land in a deserted field to offload its cargo of drugs. But often the pilot will merely throw it overboard or send it down by parachute. The profits are so vast that the loss of a few planes is an incidental expense. In 1987 the US Air Force spent $45,600,000 to catch planes being used to smuggle drugs into America. That $45,600,000 resulted in two drug busts.

An advisory report from the Committee on Law Reform of the New York County Lawyers' Association estimates that drug prohibition causes at least 7,100 deaths a year – including 75 gang war murders, 3,500 deaths from AIDS by people who used dirty needles and the addicts who die because of poisoned or dirty black-market drugs. In America the drugs war leads to around 750,000 arrests every year but three-quarters of those are drug users arrested for possession. Courts are clogged, other trials are delayed and $90 billion are spent to arrest people who simply use drugs. The Committee estimates that the American economy loses $80 billion a year as a result of the drugs war.

Those who support the drugs war often claim that they are trying to protect the public from a great danger. But in America the annual number of deaths from cocaine, heroin and cannabis is between three and four thousand, whereas the number of people who die from using cigarettes and alcohol is over one hundred times as great. The use of legal, prescription drugs kills far more people than the use of illegal drugs. In America heart drugs alone are said to kill 125,000 people a year.

Some politicians argue that the problems associated with heroin, cocaine and cannabis and other drugs would get worse if they were decriminalized. But is that true? It seems not. The New York County Lawyers' Association estimates that decriminalization would not lead to any increase in the number of deaths. Indeed, they claim that America would need an impossible 2200 per cent increase in illegal drug use to produce as many deaths as the drugs war already produces. Remember, that according to the New York County Lawyers' Association drug prohibition kills at least 7,100 people a year whereas illegal drug use leads to (according to the latest figures) 3,652 deaths a year. Society's efforts to stamp out illegal drug use leads to gangsterism, the loss of civil liberties, huge expenses and more deaths of innocent people. The gangster's profits rise and society's costs rise not despite but because of the drugs war. The money that is being spent on drug control is not just failing to do anything useful – it is making things considerably worse.

In practice, experience suggests that laws do not stop people using drugs or dealing in them. On the contrary, our clumsy attempts to legislate against drug use have almost certainly made things considerably worse rather than better. The damage done by prohibition in the United States is an excellent example of the way in which drug control laws can backfire.

One of the commonest problems with drug legislation is that it frequently seems quite arbitrary when looked at dispassionately, and different nations hardly ever agree on what seems fair or proper. It is important to remember that in the nineteenth century the British (in collusion with the French) fought two wars to protect their right to keep selling opium to the Chinese.

Drugs which are sold freely in one country may be banned in another country. We in the west have no right to condemn this since one of our freely available drugs (alcohol) is illegal in many other countries. The variations in customs and legislation make things easy for smugglers and drug dealers who can always find somewhere safe from which to operate. Those who criticize countries in which drugs are prepared for illegal export often fail to understand the extent of the pressure on local politicians and law enforcers. In Colombia, for example, judges and newspaper editors are offered a 'free' choice by the drug barons. They are invited to accept a bribe of $100,000 and to look the other way. Or, they are told, you can cause trouble in which case we will shoot your family. These are not idle threats. It is easy to be brave when not exposed to threats of this kind and easier still to pass judgements on those who have not acted in the way we in the comfortable west like to think we would have acted.

Another reason for being wary about drug control legislation is the fact that many drug users are actually attracted to an illegal drug *because* it is illegal. In *Umanita Nova* in 1922, Errico Malatesta wrote:

> The more severe the penalties imposed on the consumers and traffickers of cocaine, the greater will be the attraction of forbidden fruits and the fascination of the risks incurred by the consumer, and the greater will be the profits made by the speculators, avid for money. It is useless, therefore, to hope for anything from the law. We must suggest other solutions. Make the use and sale of cocaine free from restrictions, and open kiosks where it would be sold at cost price or even under cost. And then launch a great propaganda campaign to explain to the public . . . The harmful use of cocaine would not disappear completely . . . but . . . the evil would decrease, because nobody could make profits out of its sale, and nobody could speculate on the hunt for speculators . . . Our suggestion either will not be taken into

account, or it will be considered impractical and mad. Yet intelligent and disinterested people might say to themselves: since the penal laws have proved to be impotent, would it not be a good thing, as an experiment, to try out the anarchist method?

Malatesta was right. The American experience during prohibition should have shown us that more laws don't stop drug abuse but merely make it more exciting and more profitable.

The main shortcoming of drug control legislation is not that it is arbitrary or that it glamorizes drug taking but that it doesn't deal with the source of the problem: the forces which drive people to use drugs. However much legislation is passed and however many drug enforcement officers are recruited, the need for drugs will remain as long as our society remains rich in stress. By forcing drug users to buy their supplies illegally, the law changes the social status of the drug user from stressed but law-abiding citizen to hunted criminal. For the first time in his life the drug user will start mixing with members of the underworld and will begin to associate with them and learn their standards. Because the cost of the drugs he uses gets higher and higher so he (or she) has to turn to illegal methods to obtain the cash he (or she) needs. Prostitution, drug pushing and theft are the three most common ways in which drug users obtain the money they need.

In one study done in Philadelphia, each addict in a group of 237 committed an average of 192 crimes every year in order to support his (or her) habit. The National Institute of Drug Abuse in America conducted a study in Baltimore which showed that 243 male heroin addicts had been responsible for 500,000 crimes in an eleven-year period. The Institute estimate that in America male drug addicts are responsible for over 40,000,000 crimes a year. Studies done by the Department of Justice have shown that over half of all property crimes are drug-related with 42 per cent of bank robberies being committed by drug users. Those who favour tough laws to control drug use often argue that the drug war is justified because of the close links between drug use and crime but what they fail to understand is that drugs and crime are linked *because* of the drug control laws. The crime on the streets which is associated with drugs in America (and to a lesser but a growing extent in Europe) is not a direct result of drug use per se but is a direct result of the fact that the use of drugs is illegal.

Sadly, there is also plenty of evidence to show that those who are paid to pursue and arrest the drug traffickers are frequently tempted by the amount of money involved. There is probably no other activity which comes close to producing so much corruption among politicians and law enforcement officers and there are probably not many police forces or customs forces anywhere in the world that have not been tainted by corruption. The stakes are high and for drug smugglers the easiest (and cheapest) way to avoid detection is to 'buy off' the police. Drug smugglers only need one dishonest officer in a force for the local drugs war to fail. If drug smugglers can buy up whole governments (which they certainly can do) then buying up a few poorly paid police officers is not going to be difficult.

The drugs business has been described as the cause of most of the world's largest criminal conspiracies as well as of most of its petty crime. In America in one three year period in the 1980s three hundred high-level government law enforcement officials were publicly implicated in drug related corruption. In one town the chief of police, the sheriff, a judge and the manager of the local airport formed a ring to provide an escort service for drug traffickers arriving at the local airport. At least one Supreme Court Judge is on the run accused of drug smuggling. In Bolivia a general was reputed to receive $150,000 a week for allowing air force planes to transport coca paste to Colombia; and it was not all that long ago that members of one government stopped drug smuggling flights because they thought that their bribes were too low. Numerous high-ranking police officers around the world have been accused not simply of turning a blind eye to drug smuggling but of organizing drug rackets.

The tragedy of modern police activity is that it often leads to the arrest of the drug user or the small-time pusher rather than the supplier who will inevitably be well organized, living in a 'safe' country and almost impossible to catch. Most big suppliers are not addicts and they do not deal on the streets. They use aeroplanes and boats and hire couriers to do the dangerous work and are safe from the relatively short arm of the law. The 'leaders' of organized crime, the 'businessmen', do not risk arrest. They hire other people to take the chances and, like many honest businessmen, they are prepared to take chances and accept a certain level of losses. Small-time drug users who recognize that they are already breaking the law are quite prepared to take the extra risk involved in becoming a drug pusher since they reckon that if they are caught they are going to be punished anyway. When the police do catch a small-time user and pusher they invariably describe him as an 'international drugs dealer' in order to make their effort look worthwhile. Time and time again, in every country where the drugs war is fought, months of planning, millions of pounds and huge amounts of police effort end up with a handful of arrests and a pocketful of drugs being confiscated.

In England a recent massive police raid involving around six hundred police officers was widely described as an important 'drugs bust'. In practice the six hundred police officers spent hours fighting with enormous crowds and eventually found just two-and-a-half pounds of cannabis. The violence that ensued led to the majority of the court appearances which followed. There was no real disruption of supply or usage and the drug raid effectively produced nothing more than some social disruption and an increased hatred of the police. In 1978 British policemen from ten separate forces helped to arrest 29 people accused of making 60 million doses of LSD – half the western world's supply of the drug. It was predicted that with the main supplier out of business the street price of LSD would rocket – but within two weeks another supplier had taken over and the price hardly budged.

Even when a dealer of medium importance does get caught, the penalties allowed in a civilized world seem strangely inappropriate. For example, one drug smuggler who made a personal fortune of £250,000,000 – working alone – was given a seven-year jail sentence when he was caught. There cannot be many professional criminals who would not be prepared to risk a seven-year jail sentence if they thought they could make that much money. Undercover officers will never get close to the gang bosses because most if not all gangs favour initiation ceremonies in which new members are only accepted – and trusted – when they have been seen to kill at least one person. Today just about every illegal or criminal organization in the world – from the mafia to the triad – bank rolls, manages or takes a cut from the drug trade.

The inefficiency of the drug enforcement agencies is illustrated only too vividly by the fact that in most countries the price of drugs such as heroin and cocaine is steadily falling, suggesting that more and more supplies are being successfully moved past customs posts. A report sponsored by the United States Defense Department in the late 1980s argued that smugglers have so many methods of bringing in drugs that expanding interception techniques will not make very much – if any – difference, while attempts to bring military equipment into the equation are doomed since the forces are not well suited to fighting a drugs war. After a shipment of 3906 pounds of cocaine was seized, the enforcement agencies expected the street price of cocaine to go up. It did – temporarily – but within a couple of days the price was back to normal and one enforcement agent admitted that the drug barons in Colombia had merely sent another batch from their stockpile to replace the one which had been intercepted. Customs and police officers around the world admit that they seize approximately five per cent of the drugs that are being smuggled. Many experts argue that this is an optimistic estimate.

The other risk that the drug user has to face because of the law is that the type of drug he buys may be more dangerous than the type of drug he bought before. Buyers obtaining drugs illegally are in no position to complain about the strength or quality of the product they are purchasing. Governments can compel manufacturers to ensure that their products are well made and consistent in quality. But banned drugs are banned – and there is no quality control. Cheap cocaine is often poisoned by petrol used as a solvent when it is being made. The petrol can – and does – kill. In southern Italy the mafia sells heroin at a 10 per cent concentration, while in the north of Italy heroin is sold at a 50 per cent concentration: when addicts from the south visit the north they frequently kill themselves when they mistakenly inject a far too powerful drug. The hillworkers of the Andes were turned from using coca leaf to cocaine because the law made the leaf too valuable and showed the profits to be made out of selling illegal cocaine. The opium users of China were turned to heroin because of the law. In both cases the traditional, legal product was much safer and it was also free of pollutants and toxic side effects.

The final irony is that when the law *is* sustained many drug users are turned from using illegal drugs to using far more lethal legal drugs. In China in the 1950s a massive campaign was launched to eliminate opium usage. Heavy legal controls were introduced and people suspected of using opium were locked up without trial. The result was that huge numbers of opium users switched to using a legal drug – tobacco. The Chinese government was happy about this because of the profit it made. The end result was that today the Chinese people are beginning to show signs of tobacco-induced cancer and heart disease for the first time. Smoking opium is relatively harmless and the Chinese people have been converted to smoking tobacco – which kills – by the law.

In America a major supermarket chain announced in the summer of 1991 that it had decided to sell packets of cigarette papers only if customers also bought pouches of tobacco. They did this because it was alleged that some customers were buying the cigarette papers in order to roll marijuana cigarettes. It seems likely that the new rule will simply lead to the increase in use of a substance – tobacco – that is far more dangerous than marijuana. Another 'victory' for the law.

The simplistic, traditional police approach to drug use is to put everyone in prison and confiscate everything belonging to anyone who uses drugs. This simple-minded approach does not work. Laws simply isolate some drug users from other members of society and make their personal problems worse. For most of this century numerous attempts have been made to control drug use and drug addiction. The League of Nations, the United Nations and the World Health Organization have all tried to outlaw the use of many drugs. Individual governments have introduced masses of legislation and have frequently announced that the war against drug use will be expanded. Numerous American presidents and other leaders have made powerful promises about ending the drugs war but have made no difference to the size of the problem. Governments refuse to face reality because reality is embarrassing and politically unacceptable.

Despite all the effort, the size of the world's drug abuse problem has continued to grow and in the long run the problem of drug addiction will only be solved by improving the standards of the society in which we all live. The truth is that even if the war was partly won and the quantity of drugs getting through went down, the crime rate would go up if drugs remained illegal – because the same number of crooks would be fighting for survival, prices would have to go up and the addicts needing drugs would have to commit more crimes to pay for the drugs they needed.

A successful drugs war would not mean that drug supplies would dry up completely and it would not mean that the number of addicts would necessarily fall. It is impossible to envisage a situation in a free world where law enforcement officers could abolish drug use or drug smuggling completely. All they can hope to do is to make smuggling more difficult and drug use more dangerous. Is that really going to help? The evidence suggests not.

Our drug laws have given us a war which has provided employment for a vast number of law enforcement officers, has eroded our civil liberties, and has endangered the public health. (Because drug use is illegal, society cannot provide users with clean syringes and so drug addicts use dirty ones and spread diseases such as AIDS and hepatitis. In America one quarter of all cases of AIDS are among self-injectors using dirty needles, and in New York more than half the intravenous drug addicts are infected with the AIDS virus because they have shared needles. In Edinburgh in Scotland the high incidence of AIDS and hepatitis B is directly related to the high incidence of needle sharing.) This war has also cost every one of us a small fortune in cash, and has cost many honest men and women their freedom or their lives. Our drug control laws lead to drug users mixing their 'fix' with water taken from a lavatory bowl in a public toilet because they are so frightened of being caught with a drug in their pocket that they dare not take it home with them.

Consider, for example, the way in which our civil liberties have been eroded by the increasingly hysterical prosecution of a patently ineffective drugs war. Even if we ignore the fact that there is something strange about a legal system which seems determined to persecute individuals who choose to grow and smoke their own cannabis in private but which is, nevertheless, quite happy to allow citizens to undertake far more hazardous activities in public (for example: sky diving, parachuting, bunjee rope jumping, deep sea diving) without punishing them, there is no doubt that the ordinary citizen's freedoms have been severely affected by the drugs war. Law enforcement officers around the world pursue drug users and pushers with tremendous zeal (often the frustration they feel at being unable to outwit the drug smugglers is turned into a determination to catch and lock up as many users as possible) and at their request laws are frequently created to give them more power. In Britain the 1971 Act gave the police the right to stop, search and detain anyone reasonably suspected of possessing a controlled drug. The police also have the authority to burst into people's homes without warning if they suspect that there may be drugs on the premises.

All around the world ordinary citizens have discovered that these new drug control laws are beginning to affect them as much as the drug users or drug smugglers. In Jamaica flower growers trying to make a living by flying fresh flowers into the United States have encountered insurmountable problems because customs officers looking for hidden drugs keep the flowers so long that they die before they reach their destination. In America high school students have been strip searched merely because there have been reports that drugs have been used in their schools and nine thousand Army personnel have been discharged for failing drug tests even though the authorities now admit that around half of those tests were flawed because some widely prescribed medicines show up as marijuana.

The hysteria whipped up by politicians and by police officers looking for more power and more funds has created an atmosphere in which long-established human rights have been abandoned. In many countries body searches without any reasonable cause are now accepted as readily as are roadblocks and imprisonment without trial. On the Canadian border a woman had her car confiscated because customs officials managed to dig an almost invisible quantity of cannabis out of her handbag with the aid of a pair of tweezers. We have abandoned our rights and social values for a purposeless cause. As the New York County Lawyers' Association put it recently:

> We once had a society in which the very thought of men and women being strip searched and forced to urinate in front of witnesses was revolting. That now seems like a long time ago. And all this for a policy that simply does not work.

In the United Kingdom asset confiscation measures introduced under the Drugs Trafficking Offences Act were criticized in the *Criminal Law Review* for abandoning the traditional principles of English justice. In America salmon fisherman Kevin Hogan discovered the cost of the anti-drug war at first hand when Customs Service agents seized his brand new fishing boat after allegedly finding 1.7 grams of marijuana in a crew member's jacket. The customs officers admitted that Hogan knew nothing about the drug and they did not charge him with any offence, but they refused to release the boat until he paid a $10,000 fine and fired the crew member.

In 1859, in an essay called *On Liberty*, John Stuart Mill wrote that 'the only purpose for which power can be rightfully exercised over any member of a civilized community, against his will, is to prevent harm to others . . . Over himself, over his own body and mind, the individual is sovereign.' That is no longer true, thanks entirely to our drug policy.

The ultimate irony is that while society breaks itself apart in its attempt to control drug abuse, the men who are making the greatest profits out of the sale of drugs are working hard to establish for themselves a kinder, more caring reputation. When heavy rain brought flooding to parts of Peru, major drug dealer Guillermo Cardenas Davilla used his fleet of aeroplanes (normally used to carry drugs) to bring in food, supplies and construction materials. In Bolivia, Roberto Suarez Snr built and equipped hospitals, and paved roads and housed his country's poorest citizens – he also offered personally to repay Bolivia's foreign debt of $4 billion in cash. Colombian drug dealer Pablo Escobar built around four thousand houses (complete with hot and cold running water, flushing lavatories, kitchens and small gardens) and gave them away to the poor. In Thailand oriental drug baron Khun Sa has built a basketball court and swimming pool for the people of the village where he lives. In Afghanistan drug runners used their profits to finance the guerrilla war against the Russians. I quote these examples not in order to vindicate or show any sympathy for those who smuggle drugs, but to show that the picture is not quite as clear-cut as some would have us believe – and to offer yet one additional reason why the attempts from the west to suppress the production and dissemination of illegal drugs are often not treated enthusiastically by the inhabitants of countries where drug production is a major industry.

7 | The only way ahead

Our drug control laws are illogical, unsound, unfair, discriminatory, expensive, impossible to enforce and counter-productive. The evidence confirms that they do more harm than good. But, contrary to the fears of some politicians, abolishing the drug control laws and decriminalizing drugs need not mean an increase in the amount of drug taking.

There is no doubt that drug addiction of one sort of another is the major plague of the twentieth century. We have created a world in which we are exposed to enormous amounts of stress, but we have not evolved fast enough to enable us to cope with the type of stress we have created. And we have created a variety of technologies and industries which are devoted to finding ways for us to forget our anxieties and frustrations. Scientists have enabled us to refine tobacco, opium and cocaine and to produce infinitely more dangerous products from natural resources which are relatively harmless in themselves. The result is that every year millions of people die because of their addictions.

And yet our attempts to use legislation to control the use of drugs have been pitifully unsuccessful. We have created a mess of laws which are based purely on prejudice, convenience and political expediency. Because these laws are not based on logic or good scientific sense they make the use of some virtually harmless products punishable by long terms of imprisonment

The Drugs Myth

and allow, or in some cases even encourage, the use of some of the most dangerous and toxic substances known. The vast majority of the millions who die through the use of drugs die through the use of legal drugs.

In our desperate attempts to deal with the plague of addiction, we have made a number of fundamental mistakes. We have assumed that when people become addicted their primary problem is a medical one, and we have organized our attempts to deal with them accordingly. The truth is that an addiction is a symptom, not a disease; and it is a symptom of a social problem, not a medical one. If we treat the addiction, we remove the symptoms, but the basic problem remains unchanged. It should not surprise us if the symptoms come back. They come back not necessarily because the substance to which the individual is addicted is physically or physiologically irresistible but because the basic problem remains unchanged. If we judge the severity of an addiction by the number of people involved and by the difficulty those people have in breaking their addiction, then the most addictive substance known to humankind is food. Since it is clear that food is not 'addictive' in the strict sense of the word, it must also be clear that people who are addicted to overeating food must be addicted because it helps them deal with, suppress or forget their problems in some way.

Similarly, we have made the mistake of assuming that when the symptoms of an addiction differ, then the treatment that is needed must differ too. The truth is that because all types of addictions are symptoms, and are indeed consequences of a relatively limited number of fairly similar basic problems, the long-term solution is not to look for more or better cures but to search for ways to deal with the problems.

It is through these fundamental errors that we have arrived at two more major misconceptions: that there must be medical and legal solutions to the problem of addiction. These misconceptions have led us to make a number of important mistakes. For example, in our search for medical cures for addiction we have produced an apparently endless series of more sophisticated, more powerful and more dangerous drugs. Almost inevitably those therapeutic drugs themselves then lead to addiction. Morphine was introduced as a cure for opium addiction. Heroin was introduced as a cure for morphine addiction.

Methadone was introduced as a cure for heroin addiction. The barbiturates were offered as a replacement for the addictive bromides. The benzodiazepines were introduced as a non-addictive alternative to the barbiturates. And the world's drug companies are now busy searching for a new replacement for the benzodiazepines. Doctors have consistently made the world's addiction problem worse by over-prescribing and by failing to understand the needs and weaknesses of the human organism. *Drug addiction of all kinds will be eradicated not when doctors introduce a new 'wonder' drug but when society eradicates inequality, frustration, envy and injustice.*

Meanwhile we have made things far, far worse by our attempts to eradicate addiction by using the law. Our crude and ill thought out attempts to outlaw the use of drugs which are not produced, marketed or supported by powerful international industries have exacerbated underlying social problems of alienation, frustration, loneliness and fear; created economic problems in many countries; damaged personal freedoms and civil liberties; increased the power of the bully in most so-called civilized countries and divided the rich from the poor, the young from the old and the weak from the strong.

While the politicians and legislators have introduced a plethora of confusing and contradictory laws designed to control the use of drugs which were deemed unacceptable over half a century ago (for quite arbitrary reasons, as we have seen), the producers and manufacturers of truly damaging but perfectly legal drugs such as alcohol and tobacco have seen to it that their markets have continued to grow.

In many countries alcohol is now more widely consumed than it has ever been before and low taxes mean that it is cheaper too.

Similarly, tobacco companies are finding it easy to continue to sell their products. European governments may occasionally announce that they would like to see stricter controls on advertizing but when it comes to the crunch they do nothing that will annoy the tobacco companies. Indeed, tobacco producers in Europe receive hundreds of millions of pounds a year in subsidies so that they can produce *more* tobacco at more attractive prices. How can anyone have respect for governments which exhibit hypocrisy at these levels?

The Drugs Myth

Those who support the existing attempts to control the sale of drugs such as heroin, cocaine and cannabis with the aid of the law should ask themselves a few quite simple questions.

First, they should ask themselves why these particular drugs should be selected for legal control. It cannot possibly be because they are more dangerous than any other substances. Our evidence has shown, quite clearly, that heroin, cocaine and cannabis are considerably safer to use than either alcohol or tobacco. Would it be fair to put smokers in prison and to deprive them of their cigarettes quite forcibly? Is there any sense in forcing heroin users to buy their drugs illegally and then punishing them for breaking the law? Our arbitrary selection of illegal drugs means that those who use these products have to take up crime and behave in a persistently deviant way, thus substantiating the myth that drug users are crooks, deviants and social misfits.

Second, they should ask themselves whether the laws are working, or are ever likely to work, and whether the advantages of the laws outweigh the disadvantages. The answer is fairly clear. Most governments have put an enormous amount of effort into controlling the marketing and use of heroin, cocaine, cannabis and other drugs branded as illegal. But those attempts have proved entirely useless. Despite the huge armies of people involved in drug control, the price of drugs has come down and the number of addicts has gone up. The American experience during prohibition should have taught us all a lesson. Drug control laws make drug use exciting for many users and more profitable for drug dealers. You cannot legislate against drug use any more than you can legislate against people paying money for sex. The drug control laws simply create a greater criminal class. Attempts to control the sale and use of drugs have given more power to the police and have drastically reduced the freedom of all law-abiding citizens as well as law breakers. The phenomenal social, human and financial cost of drug control laws cannot possibly be defended.

Third, they should ask themselves whether or not the laws save any lives. The facts show that they do not. Indeed, by making these drugs illegal we are exposing those who use them to greater risks. If heroin, cocaine and cannabis were sold without the law interfering, it would be possible to control the quality. The number of accidental overdoses would fall and far fewer users would be made ill by poisonous contaminants. In addition, if we decriminalized the use of drugs such as heroin and cocaine we would be able to provide addicts with clean syringes and needles – this would lead to a dramatic reduction in the incidence of AIDS and hepatitis among drug users.

Those who support our present legal position should ask themselves if they can think of *any* purpose to the laws which exist. The evidence shows that the laws are unfair, illogical, ineffective and counterproductive. Why do we continue to spend so much energy and so much effort in trying to control drugs which do comparatively little harm?

If our drug laws were abandoned and all drug use was decriminalized (there is, incidentally, a subtle but important difference between legalization and decriminalization – the former suggests legal approval of drug taking, the latter a simple absence of punishment), we would have far more money to spend on improving society and on reducing the need for people to take drugs. We would have several billion dollars and pounds available simply through abandoning our drug wars. And we would, in addition, have whatever income we choose to raise by putting taxes on drugs such as cocaine, heroin and cannabis. At the moment drug smuggling is one of the biggest industries in the world; the profits made are vast. If drugs were decriminalized then they could be sold in clean, hygienic form for a fraction of their present price, but they could also be quite heavily taxed. Tax laws are relatively easy to use as controls. Al Capone was eventually arrested and imprisoned because of tax infringements rather than because of any of his other crimes. He had been allegedly involved in two hundred gangland killings and indicted on numerous occasions – once for over five thousand prohibition violations – but witnesses kept disappearing and charges kept getting dropped until 1931 when he was jailed for eleven years on twenty-two counts of tax evasion.

By raising tax rates it is possible to control the use of drugs far more effectively. History shows that the most effective way to control the use of any drug is to tax it. During the industrial revolution in England cheap, poisonous gin was killing thousands and ruining industrial efficiency – so the government forced distillers to sell good quality liquor and then taxed them

115

on it. Tax rates can be used to divert demand from the worst types of drugs – and the most dangerous drugs – to less dangerous substances. Taxes actually discourage drug use, too, and there is a strong link between drug prices and consumption. In 1690 in Britain, for example, the duty on beer was tripled and consumption fell by a third. In 1791 another tripling of the duty on beer meant that the consumption went down by a quarter. In the nineteenth century alcohol got cheaper and consumption went up. Today alcohol is comparatively cheap and consumption is, once again, high.

Taxes can also ensure that the costs involved in policing the trade of a drug, for treating victims and for ensuring the quality of substances remains good, are met by those who are selling the products – and making the profits. At the moment the drug barons pay nothing in taxes and nothing towards the cost of treatment. By banning drugs, governments abandon the most effective means of controlling them and lose their chance of raising funds to help fight drug use. However high taxes were raised, prices would almost certainly remain lower than illegal prices and so there would be less need for drug addicts to commit crimes to pay for their drugs.

Decriminalizing drugs would wipe out the huge drug gangs and would dramatically reduce the number of people persuaded to try drugs by pushers anxious to give away free samples and entice more non-users into becoming customers. There are no illegal suppliers of tobacco or alcohol today, for the very simple reason that these drugs are too readily available over the shop counter.

Most important of all, it would be possible to use some of the money raised by taxes to organize a series of massive campaigns designed to discourage people from using any sort of drugs at all. At the moment we are spending ever increasing amounts of money on trying to stop drug use, ever decreasing amounts on trying to help drug users break their habit, and nothing at all on trying to improve social conditions so that people don't get tempted to take drugs. By changing our legal approach we would have far more money to spend on preventing drug addiction of all kinds developing; after all, the most effective way of treating the drug problem must be to tackle the underlying problems which lead to drug use.

The only way ahead

In conclusion, the only logical way to deal with the world's drug addiction plague is to repeal all drug control laws and to introduce taxation together with a massive, international campaign. We could, for example, ensure that all drugs (tobacco, alcohol, cocaine, cannabis, heroin and so on) had to be sold from 'official' drug centres. And we could make those centres dull and boring. How many people would be addicted to tobacco or alcohol if you could only buy those drugs in places that looked like tax offices? Addicts would be able to buy their drugs readily enough but how many people would *start* an addiction under those circumstances?

Decriminalization will undoubtedly produce some problems of its own; but decriminalization is a far more honest, honourable and sensible answer to our problem. Sadly, we live in a world in which for many people drugs are a necessary escape and the only viable alternative to misery, loneliness and frustration. Our present, crude attempts at repression simply make things worse for everyone. Drug control laws make a bad business worse; they made drug use criminal as well as sad and they make drug use dangerous. They also make the sale of drugs more attractive and more profitable.

All drugs are bad for people. In an ideal world no one would take psychoactive drugs purely to help them forget or escape. Tobacco and alcohol kill the people who use them and kill their friends too. Heroin, cocaine and cannabis endanger people by putting them into contact with the criminal underworld. But our world is not ideal. And until politicians have the insight, courage and determination to combat injustice, cruelty and the other causes of stress, anxiety and unhappiness people will continue to take drugs. Making laws will not make any useful difference. All we can do is to try to persuade as many people as possible to take the drugs which do the least amount of harm.

Some people who have thought about decriminalization believe that we should begin by decriminalizing cannabis alone – leaving heroin and cocaine and the other illegal drugs as illegal.

I think this would be disastrous.

The gangsters who currently sell cannabis would have no alternative but to concentrate all their resources on selling drugs which were still illegal. They would, inevitably, put pressure on their customers to switch away from cannabis and to start using heroin, cocaine or something else. The billionaire drug barons would not stop trading just because *one* drug had been legalized. And the consequences would be awful. Within weeks the number of people using heroin and cocaine would have multiplied dramatically, though the prices would have probably come down as the drug barons used their stock piles to enable them to fight for a big share of the new business. I can see the attraction of moving step by step and decriminalizing cannabis alone, but it really would be a terrible move.

So, how should we go about decriminalizing drugs? And if we decriminalize all drugs, what will happen? Won't the streets be filled with heroin addicts and cocaine pushers if we decriminalize all the drugs which are currently illegal?

The truth is disarmingly simple. All we have to do is to abandon our laws, introduce taxes for all drugs, begin a well thought out and honest campaign warning people of the dangers of *all* drugs, and then let the market forces operate. In America after prohibition the consumption of alcohol dropped by a staggering fifty per cent. I believe that the consumption of heroin, cocaine and cannabis would fall by a comparable amount within a very short time.

All advertizing for all drugs (including tobacco and alcohol) could and should be banned. With billions of dollars released for a sensible, practical and honest worldwide anti-drug campaign the abuse of psychoactive substances would plummet within months.

A proven success

If those who are reluctant to abandon their prejudices, preconceived notions and myth-based fears need extra comfort, it is available; for in Holland drug control attitudes and laws have already been softened and the consequences have not substantiated the widely and loudly broadcast fears of those who oppose decriminalization. In 1976 the Dutch made the sale of small amounts of cannabis a minor misdemeanour rather on the level of a parking offence. The courts and the police decided to turn a blind eye to cannabis use. It was a daring move but it worked. In 1976 15 per cent of the population between the ages of 13 and 25 in Holland were using cannabis. After the laws controlling the drug were softened, the number using the drug fell to between one and two per cent. Cannabis is cheap but there is less crime than there would be if the same number of people were drinking alcohol. Mugging and violent street crimes are relatively rare in Amsterdam. People worry about cannabis users only in case they go on to use tobacco – which is widely recognized to be far more dangerous. Because cannabis is cheap to buy there is no related crime.

The police in Holland still have the power to arrest those selling or using hard drugs such as heroin and cocaine but since 1985 the Ministry of Justice has advised the police to back off. They believe that enforcement turns a health problem into a crime problem and that as long as trade is open the drug sellers can be observed and the drug users helped when they are in trouble. There is now no need for drug traffickers to bribe policemen and prices are relatively cheap. There is no need for gang wars. Despite the freedom the use of cocaine in Amsterdam is falling. Cocaine use is three times as common in New York, where it is illegal, as it is in Amsterdam.

The Dutch have not repealed their drug control laws but they do ignore them; their approach is pragmatic rather than revolutionary; they have adapted and they have integrated drug addicts into their community to everyone's benefit; they have not officially legalized drugs usually regarded as illegal elsewhere but they collect taxes on the sale of cannabis. They are still signatories of the international drug control conventions but they no longer try to stop drug use within their borders.

A quarter of the AIDS patients in America are intravenous drug users. In Holland only 8 per cent of AIDS patients are drug users. A greater percentage of Americans use cannabis (which is expensive, illegal to buy and illegal to use) than of the Dutch (who can buy it easily and cheaply). One Dutch aim was to integrate drug programmes so that alcoholics and smokers could be helped alongside other addicts. They have achieved this aim. Another aim was to take the glamour out of drug use. They have done that too. And a third successful aim was to separate hard and soft drugs. According to *The Lancet* addiction is 'not on the increase in Holland'. More important 'a continuing increase in the average age of addicts (just over 30 now) suggests that fewer people are being lured into addiction'.

Dr Frits Ruter, professor of criminal law at Amsterdam University, has compared the results of the Dutch approach to drug use with the very hard-line German approach. He has shown that cannabis use is decreasing in Holland but increasing in Germany – which now has three times as many addicts as Holland and over twice as many deaths from drug overdoses. In addition Professor Ruter has shown that the crime rate in Holland has not increased in recent years while murder rates in Amsterdam are less than a tenth of murder rates in Washington DC. Dr Ruter claims that the law, and law enforcement officers, are not well suited for a fight against drug trafficking – partly because demand creates supply and provides the incentive to do what the law prohibits, and partly because criminal law has never succeeded in completely eliminating any forbidden behaviour.

Prohibition is a proven failure. Decriminalization may not be the perfect solution, but where it has been tried, it is a proven success. Sadly, we do not live in a perfect world (which is, of course, why drug use is so commonplace), but while decriminalization does not mean giving in to the drug dealers, it does mean finding a new and better way of beating them. Decriminalization will enable us to differentiate between the people who use drugs and those who sell them. Decriminalization is not an endorsement of drug use or drug abuse but it is a recognition that all drug use is a consequence not of evil but of a sadness and of a need that deserves sympathy, understanding and support, not simple disapproval. Decriminalization would enable us to offer treatment programmes and support that would help us dramatically to reduce the incidence of disease and illness among those using drugs which are currently illegal. Decriminalization would free money and resources which would enable us to combat *all* drug use – including that of drugs which are currently regarded as legal. Decriminalization would enable us to end many of the misleading and confusing variations in drug laws around the world and it would enable us to provide drug users with advice that they just might listen to.

The only way ahead

Repression has failed. Decriminalization would enable us to help drug users without the short and violent arm of the law interfering. Our present system, based on force and hypocrisy, does not work, has never worked and never will work.